D1207861

INTRODUCTION TO REAL ANALYSIS

Harper's Series in Modern Mathematics

I. N. Herstein and Gian-Carlo Rota, Editors

HARPER & ROW, Publishers

New York, Evanston, and London

INTRODUCTION TO REAL ANALYSIS

by **CASPER GOFFMAN**

Division of Mathematical Sciences
Purdue University

INTRODUCTION TO REAL ANALYSIS

 For information address Harper & Row, Publishers, Incorporated, 49 East 33rd Street, New York, N.Y. 10016.

Library of Congress Catalog Card Number: 66-14166

TO GITTIE

CONTENTS

PREFACE

It is my hope that this book, together with my *Calculus of Several Variables,* will furnish a treatment of real analysis adequate for the training of advanced undergraduates. On the other hand, the two books remain largely independent.

In this book, the processes of analysis are introduced and are used to obtain simple, but interesting and important, mathematical facts. The real number system is treated by means of modified Dedekind cuts. The real numbers are then identified as a complete ordered field, and it is noted that all the properties of the real numbers follow from this fact. It is thus possible for the instructor to start a course with the second chapter, with perhaps some remarks regarding the contents of the first chapter. A one semester course might be built around Chapters 2, 4, 6, 7, and 8, together with as many selections from the other chapters as time permits.

Exercises are given at the end of each chapter, numbered according to the section to which the exercise relates. Thus, the exercise number 3.7 is concerned with the material of section 3 of the given chapter. Many of the exercises are simple and are intended to give the reader practice. Some exercises are more difficult and will test the skill and ingenuity of the reader. It is important that exercises of this type be included, since part of mathematical training consists in developing power to do mathematics.

J. E. Diem and W. J. Gorman have read the manuscript with great care. I am grateful to them for the many suggestions they made, on the basis of which the text was amended. I would like to thank Judy Snider for performing the difficult job of typing the manuscript.

C.G.

May, 1966

INTRODUCTION TO REAL ANALYSIS

CHAPTER I

THE REAL NUMBERS

1. SETS, NOTATION

We shall be concerned with sets of numbers, sets of functions, etc. Sets will usually be designated by capital letters $A, B, C, \cdots$. The elements of a set will usually be designated by lower-case letters $a, b, c, \cdots$. If a is an element of A, we say that *a belongs to A*, and write

$$a \in A.$$

If a does not belong to A, we write

$$a \notin A.$$

If A and B are sets and every element of A is an element of B, we say that A is a **subset** of B or that A is *contained in* B, and write

$$A \subset B.$$

We also say that B **contains** A, and write

$$B \supset A.$$

If $A \subset B$ and $A \neq B$, we say that A is a **proper subset** of B. Thus, A is a proper subset of B if $a \in A$ implies $a \in B$ and there is an $a \in B$ such that $a \notin A$.

In most considerations, all sets which arise will be subsets of a certain set S. For every $A \subset S$, the **complement** of A, relative to S, is the set, $\mathscr{C}A$, of all $x \in S$ such that $x \notin A$. We shall use the notation

$$\mathscr{C}A = [x: x \in S, x \notin A].$$

The complement $\mathscr{C}S$ of S itself is the empty set $\varnothing$ which has no elements. Moreover, the complement of $\varnothing$ is S.

We consider two operations on families of sets. We first define these operations, union and intersection, for pairs of sets. The **union** of two sets A and B is the set, $A \cup B$, composed of those elements belonging to at least one of the sets A or B. The **intersection** of A and B is the set $\mathbf{A} \cap \mathbf{B}$ of elements belonging to both A and B. We leave it to the reader to show that $A \cup B$ is the unique set which contains A and B and is contained in every set which contains A and B. Also, $A \cap B$ is the unique set which is contained in A and B and contains every set which is contained in A and B.

More generally, let U be a set and consider a family of sets A_u, $u \in U$. The union of the sets A_u, $u \in U$, is the set composed of those elements belonging to at least one of the A_u, and the intersection of the sets A_u, $u \in U$, is the set of elements belonging to all of the A_u. We use the notations

$$\bigcup[A_u: u \in U] \quad \text{and} \quad \bigcap[A_u: u \in U]$$

or

$$\bigcup_{u \in U} A_u \quad \text{and} \quad \bigcap_{u \in U} A_u,$$

for the union and intersection, respectively, of the sets A_u.

We prove two simple relations involving union, intersection, and complementation. Suppose the sets A_u, $u \in U$, are subsets of a set S and consider complements relative to S.

(a) $$\bigcup[A_u: u \in U] = \mathscr{C}\{\bigcap[\mathscr{C}A_u: u \in U]\}.$$

Proof

Let $x \in \bigcup[A_u: u \in U]$. Then there is a $u \in U$ such that $x \in A_u$. Then $x \notin \mathscr{C}A_u$. Thus $x \notin \bigcap[\mathscr{C}A_u: u \in U]$ so that $x \in \mathscr{C}\{\bigcap[\mathscr{C}A_u: u \in U]\}$.

Let $x \in \mathscr{C}\{\bigcap[\mathscr{C}A_u: u \in U]\}$. Then $x \notin \bigcap[\mathscr{C}A_u: u \in U]$. There is then a $u \in U$ such that $x \notin \mathscr{C}A_u$. Thus $x \in A_u$ so that $x \in \bigcup[A_u: u \in U]$. ∎

(b) $$\bigcap[A_u: u \in U] = \mathscr{C}\{\bigcup[\mathscr{C}A_u: u \in U]\}.$$

Proof

Let $x \in \bigcap[A_u: u \in U]$. Then $x \in A_u$, for every $u \in U$, so that $x \notin \mathscr{C}A_u$, for every $u \in U$. Thus, $x \notin \bigcup[\mathscr{C}A_u: u \in A]$, whence $x \in \mathscr{C}\{\bigcup[\mathscr{C}A_u: u \in U]\}$.

Let $x \in \mathscr{C}\{\bigcup[\mathscr{C}A_u: u \in U]\}$. Then $x \notin \bigcup[\mathscr{C}A_u: u \in U]$, so that $x \notin \mathscr{C}A_u$, for every $u \in U$. Thus $x \in A_u$, for every $u \in U$, so that $x \in \bigcap[A_u: u \in U]$. ∎

2. MAPPINGS

Let A and B be sets. A **mapping** f of A into B associates, with each $x \in A$, an element $f(x) \in B$. The mapping is designated by

$$f: A \to B.$$

The mapping f is said to be **injective** if $x \neq y$ implies $f(x) \neq f(y)$; f is said to be **surjective** if $z \in B$ implies there is an $x \in A$ such that $f(x) = z$. Finally, f is said to be **bijective** if it is both injective and surjective. Two sets are sometimes said to be put into one-one correspondence by a bijective mapping. If there is such a mapping the sets are said to have the **same cardinal number.**

Let $f: A \to B$ and $g: B \to C$. The **composition mapping**

$$g \circ f: A \to C$$

is defined by

$$(g \circ f)(x) = g(f(x)),$$

for every $x \in A$.

It is obvious that if f and g are bijective then so is $g \circ f$. Hence, if A and B have the same cardinal number and if B and C have the same cardinal number, then A and C have the same cardinal number.

3. ORDERED SETS. NATURAL NUMBERS

Let S be a set. An **order relation,** $\leq$, defined for pairs in S, is assumed to satisfy the conditions

(*i*) For every $a \in S$ and $b \in S$, either $a \leq b$ or $b \leq a$.
(*ii*) If $a \leq b$ and $b \leq a$, then $a = b$.
(*iii*) If $a \leq b$ and $b \leq c$, then $a \leq c$.

If $a \leq b$ we also write $b \geq a$. If $a \leq b$ and $a \neq b$, we write $a < b$, and $b > a$. We then say a is less than b and b is greater than a.

A set with an order relation satisfying (*i*), (*ii*), and (*iii*) is called an **ordered set.**

We shall be concerned with a special ordered set, the set of **natural numbers,** which we designate as

$$N = 1, 2, \cdots, n, \cdots.$$

We take as an axiom that there is an order relation defined on N which satisfies the following three conditions:

(a) Every nonempty subset of N has a first element, i.e., if $S \subset N$, there is an $x \in S$ such that $y \in S$ implies $y \geq x$. In particular, N itself has a first element. This element is designated by the symbol 1.

(b) Every element of N, except the first, has an immediate predecessor, i.e., if $x \in N$, $x \neq 1$, there is a $y \in N$ such that $y < x$, and if $z < x$ then $z \leq y$.

(c) N has no last element, i.e., for every $x \in N$, there is a $y \in N$ such that $x < y$.

It follows from **(a)** and **(c)** that every element of N has an immediate successor, i.e., for every $x \in N$ there is a $y \in N$ such that $y > x$ and if $z > x$ then $z \geq y$. We leave the proof to the reader.

The immediate successor of x will be designated as x'. Customary symbolism is $1' = 2$, $2' = 3, \cdots$.

A nonempty set $S \subset N$ is said to be finite if it has a last element. An arbitrary set A is said to be **finite** if there is an injective mapping of A onto a finite $S \subset N$. A nonempty set that is not finite is said to be **infinite.**

Of great importance is the so-called **principle of mathematical induction,** which we now prove.

Theorem 1

If $S \subset N$ is such that
(α) $1 \in S$, *and*
(β) $x \in S$ *implies* $x' \in S$,
then $S = N$.

Proof

Suppose $S \neq N$. Then the complement T of S, relative to N, is not empty. By (*a*), T has a first element x. Since $1 \in S$, $x \neq 1$. By (*b*), x has an immediate predecessor y. Then $y \in S$ and $y' = x \in T$. But, by (β), y' should be in S. This contradicts the assumption that $S \neq N$. Hence $S = N$. ∎

The form in which this theorem is used in practice is the following. In order to show that a certain property is possessed by all natural numbers, we need only show that 1 has the property, and that if any natural number has the property then so does its immediate successor.

We may define an operation called addition in N. This is done by defining $a + 1$ to be a' and then defining $a + b$ by induction, for every $a, b \in N$. Multiplication may be defined by letting $2a = a + a$ and then defining ba by induction. We shall not present the details.

If N and M are ordered sets which satisfy **(a)**, **(b)**, and **(c)**, it may be shown that there is a bijective mapping

$$f\colon N \to M,$$

which is order-preserving, i.e., $x > y$ implies $f(x) > f(y)$. This is accomplished by letting f map the first element of N onto the first element of M and proceeding by induction. We shall not present the details.

Let A be a set. We define a **sequence** in A to be a mapping

$$f\colon N \to A.$$

Thus, to each $x \in N$ there corresponds an $f(x) \in A$. There is a standard notation for sequences. If the set N is designated as

$$1, 2, \cdots, n, \cdots$$

the sequence is designated as

$$a_1, a_2, \cdots, a_n, \cdots,$$

where a_n is the image of n under the defining mapping. Another standard notation for a sequence is $\{a_n\}$.

It is important to distinguish between a sequence and its value set. The value set of a sequence $\{a_n\}$ is the set S such that $a_n \in S$ for some $n = 1, 2, \cdots$. The value set may consist of one element, i.e., $a_n = a_m$ for every n and m; it may be finite, or infinite.

We shall sometimes have to consider subsequences of a given sequence. For this we consider an infinite $S \subset N$. If the mapping f defines the sequence then f, restricted to S, will define the **subsequence.** If we write S as

$$n_1, n_2, \cdots, n_k, \cdots, \text{ where}$$

$$n_1 < n_2 < \cdots < n_k < \cdots,$$

then we write the subsequence as

$$a_{n_1}, a_{n_2}, \cdots, a_{n_k}, \cdots.$$

If g is the mapping which takes each k into n_k, i.e., $g(k) = n_k$ then the subsequence is given by the composition mapping

$$f \circ g.$$

4. RATIONAL NUMBERS

The rational numbers Q may be obtained in a formal way from the natural numbers. This is done by first defining integers, negative and zero as well as positive, so that subtraction may always be performed. Then the rationals are defined so that division, except by zero, may be performed. We shall not go into the construction of the rational numbers. Instead, we assume that the reader is familiar with the properties of the rationals and list these properties.

Addition and multiplication are operations in Q satisfying

1. For every $a, b \in Q$, we have $a + b \in Q$ and $ab \in Q$.
2. Both operations are commutative and associative, i.e., $a + b = b + a$, $ab = ba$, $(a + b) + c = a + (b + c)$, and $(ab)c = a(bc)$.
3. The addition operation has an identity element 0 and the multiplication operation has an identity element 1, i.e., for every $x \in Q$, we have

$$0 + x = x \quad \text{and} \quad 1 \cdot x = x.$$

4. The distributive law

$$a(b + c) = ab + ac$$

holds.

It is easy to show that $0x = 0$ for every $x \in Q$. We leave the proof to the reader.

5. The equation $a + x = b$ has a solution for every $a, b \in Q$.
6. The equation $ax = b$ has a solution for every $a, b \in Q$ with $a \neq 0$.

The solution to $a + x = 0$ is $-a$ and the solution to $ax = 1$, $a \neq 0$, is $1/a$.

The fact that the rationals satisfy the above conditions entitles the set Q of rationals to be called a **field.** The set Q is also endowed with an order structure.

7. Q is an ordered set.

The order relation, and the operations of addition and multiplication are interrelated as follows:

8. If $b \geq c$ then, for every $a \in Q$, $a + b \geq a + c$.
9. $1 > 0$.
10. If $b \geq c$ and $a \geq 0$ then $ab \geq ac$.

If $a \neq 0$, then exactly one of the two numbers a and $-a$ is positive (greater than 0) and the other is negative. This follows from 8, and the defining properties of an order relation. We add one more important property of the rational numbers.

11. Q is Archimedean, i.e., if $a > 0$ and $b > 0$ there is a natural number n such that $na > b$.

A system satisfying 1–11 is called an **Archimedean ordered field.** Thus Q is an Archimedean ordered field.

It follows that for every positive rational x there is a natural number n such that $1/n < x < n$. In particular, if a rational number is non-negative and is smaller than $1/n$, for every n, it is 0.

We associate with every rational number x its absolute value

$$|x| = \max(x, -x).$$

It follows that $|x| \geq 0$ for every x, that $|x| = |-x|$, and it is easy to prove that for every x, y,

$$|x + y| \leq |x| + |y|.$$

5. DEFECT IN THE RATIONALS

Although, as we have noted briefly above, the set of rational numbers forms a rich algebraic system, we now point out that it is inadequate for the purposes of analysis.

We first note that not every positive rational number has a rational square root.

Indeed, there is no rational number whose square is 2. In order to show this, we need only show that

$$\left(\frac{m}{n}\right)^2 \neq 2$$

for any natural numbers m and n. Now, $m = m_1 \cdot 2^r$ and $n = n_1 \cdot 2^s$ where m_1 and n_1 are odd. Then

$$m_1^2 \cdot 2^{2(r-s)} \neq 2n_1^2,$$

since m_1^2 and n_1^2 are odd, so that

$$\left(\frac{m}{n}\right)^2 = \left(\frac{m_1}{n_1}\right)^2 2^{2(r-s)} \neq 2.$$

The defect in the rationals which we wish to describe may be approached in a variety of ways. One statement is that it is possible for disjoint open intervals I and J to have no point between them.

We choose a form of the defect not quite as striking as the above, but one that is easier to work with. For this purpose, we need the notion of an open lower segment in the set of rationals. A set $J \subset Q$ is called an **open lower segment** if

(a) $J \neq \varnothing$,
(b) $J \neq Q$,
(c) for every $x \in J$, there is a $y \in J$ such that $y > x$,
(d) if $x \in J$ and $y < x$ then $y \in J$.

A point x will be called the **right end point** of an open lower segment J if

(a) for every $y \in J$, $x > y$,
(b) if z is such that for every $y \in J$, $z > y$, then $z \geq x$.

It is easy to see that if a right end point of J exists, it is unique, and is the smallest rational greater than every element of J.

We shall see that there are open lower segments without right end points in Q, and we consider this to be a defect.

A more standard equivalent approach which is not as picturesque is that a nonempty set of rational numbers which has an upper bound need not have a least upper bound (in the set of rationals). Here, an **upper bound** of a set S is a number x such that $x \geq y$ for every $y \in S$.

We now prove that Q has the defect stated above. Let J consist of all nonpositive rational numbers, together with the positive rational numbers whose square is less than 2. We show that J is an open lower segment. For this, it is only necessary to show that for every

$x \in J$ there is $y \in J$, $y > x$. Let $x > 0$ and $x^2 < 2$. There is an h such that $0 < h < 2$, and

$$x^2 + h = 2.$$

Let

$$y = x + \frac{h}{5}.$$

Then

$$\begin{aligned} y^2 = \left(x + \frac{h}{5}\right)^2 &= x^2 + \frac{2xh}{5} + \frac{h^2}{25} \\ &< x^2 + \frac{4}{5}h + \frac{2}{25}h \\ &< x^2 + h = 2. \end{aligned}$$

Thus, J is an open lower segment. We know there is no x such that $x^2 = 2$. So, if x is to be the right end point of J, then $x^2 > 2$. We show, however, that if $x^2 > 2$, $0 < x < 2$, there is $y < x$, $y > 0$ such that $y^2 > 2$. Now,

$$x^2 = 2 + h, \qquad 0 < h < 2.$$

Let

$$y = x - \frac{h}{4}.$$

Then

$$\begin{aligned} y^2 = \left(x - \frac{h}{4}\right)^2 &= x^2 - \frac{xh}{2} + \frac{h^2}{16} \\ &> x^2 - h = 2. \end{aligned}$$

Thus, there is no smallest number greater than all numbers in J, so that J has no right end point.

6. THE REAL NUMBERS

The set of real numbers is an extension of the set of rational numbers, which removes the defect described above. We will see that the real numbers are an Archimedean ordered field in which every open lower segment has a right end point.

The real numbers are obtained from the rationals by what may be described as "filling the gaps." In other words we add right end points as ideal elements, or new numbers, to correspond to those open lower segments which do not have right end points among the rationals.

One way of doing this is to consider the open, lower segment itself to be a substitute for its own right end point. One sees that this is an entirely natural approach when he agrees that open lower segments are to be in one-one correspondence with their right end points; i.e., every open lower segment is to have a right end point and distinct open lower segments must have different right end points.

In accordance with the above, the set R of real numbers is defined to be the set of open lower segments of rational numbers.

We do not intend to give the complete details, but shall give definitions of addition, multiplication, and order relation in R, and shall give some of the details showing that R is an Archimedean ordered field in which every open lower segment has a right end point.

Thus, let I and J be real numbers, i.e., open lower segments of rational numbers. Define $I + J$ as

$$I + J = [x + y: x \in I, y \in J].$$

We show that $I + J$ is an open lower segment. Let $x \in I$ and $y \in J$, so that $x + y \in I + J$, and let $u < x + y$. Then $u = x + z$, where $x \in I$ and $z < y$, so that $z \in J$. Then $u \in I + J$. Next, there is a $z > y$ such that $z \in J$. So, $x + z > x + y$ and $x + z \in I + J$. It follows that $I + J$ is an open lower segment.

It is easy to show that

$$I + J = J + I,$$

and that

$$(I + J) + K = I + (J + K).$$

Let O be the open lower segment of negative rational numbers. It is routine to verify that

$$I + \mathrm{O} = I$$

for every I.

Finally, the equation

$$I + X = J$$

has a solution for every I, J. We simply let X consist of all x such that $y + x \in J$ for every $y \in I$, except for the largest such x if there is one. The solution of $I + X = \mathrm{O}$ is designated $-I$.

An order relation is introduced in R by letting $I \geq J$ if $I \supset J$. Clearly $I > \mathrm{O}$ if and only if I contains a positive rational. That R is an ordered set is obvious.

We now define multiplication in R. If $I > O$, $J > O$ we define IJ as the set of all nonpositive rationals together with all xy where $x \in I$, $x > 0$, and $y \in J$, $y > 0$.

If $I = O$ or $J = O$ we define $IJ = O$.

If both $I < O$ and $J < O$ we define

$$IJ = (-I)(-J).$$

If exactly one of I, J is less than O, say $I < O$, we define

$$IJ = -(-I)(J)$$

It can be shown that R is an ordered field. The details are cumbersome but fairly direct and will be omitted.

Moreover, R is Archimedean. Let $I > O$, $J > O$. There is a positive rational $x \in I$ and an n such that $nx \notin J$, since Q is Archimedean. Then, it follows that $nI > J$.

The $J \in R$ for which J has a rational right end point are in one-one correspondence with the rational numbers, the associated mapping is order-preserving, and addition and multiplication preserving. That is, if we designate this injective mapping of the rationals into R by f, we have

$$f(x + y) = f(x) + f(y)$$
$$f(xy) = f(x)\ f(y)$$

and

$$x > y \quad \text{implies} \quad f(x) > f(y).$$

We then say Q is imbedded in R, or that Q is isomorphic to an ordered subfield of R. We call this subfield the rational numbers, and henceforth (except in the proof of Theorem 1) use small letters for elements of R.

We state two further facts. For any two reals x, y with $x < y$, there is a rational z such that $x < z < y$. For every real $x > 0$ there is an n such that $1/n < x$. Thus, if x is a nonnegative real such that $1/n > x$, for every n, then $x = 0$. The proofs are left to the reader.

We define open lower segments of reals and their right end points in the same way as for rationals.

Theorem 1

Every open lower segment of reals has a right end point.

Proof

Let $\mathscr{J}$ be an open lower segment of reals. Let

$$U = \bigcup[J : J \in \mathscr{J}].$$

Let $x \in U$. There is a $J \in \mathscr{J}$ such that $x \in J$. For every $y < x$, $y \in J \subset U$ and there is a $y \in J \subset U$ such that $y > x$. Moreover, there is an $I \notin \mathscr{J}$. Then $x \notin I$ implies $x \notin U$. Thus U is an open lower segment of rationals. $U \geq J$ for every $J \in \mathscr{J}$. Suppose $V \geq J$ for every $J \in \mathscr{J}$. Then $V \supset U$, so that $V \geq U$. Hence U is the right end point of $\mathscr{J}$. ∎

We give another form of Theorem 1. Let $S \subset$ R be nonempty. A number x is said to be an **upper bound** of S if $x \geq y$ for every $y \in S$.

Theorem 1′

If $S \subset$ R is nonempty and has an upper bound, it has a least upper bound.

Proof

Define a set U by letting $x \in U$ if and only if there is a $y \in S$ such that $y > x$. If $x \in U$ and $z < x$ then $z \in U$, and if $x \in U$ there is a $z \in U$ such that $z > x$. Moreover, every upper bound of S is not in U. Thus, U is an open lower segment, and so it has a right end point u.

Let $x \in S$. $y < x$ implies $y \in U$ so that $y < u$. Hence $x \leq u$. Thus, u is an upper bound of S. Let $y < u$. Then $y \in U$, so there is an $x \in S$ with $y < x$. Thus y is not an upper bound of S. ∎

A **lower bound** x of a nonempty set S is a number such that $x \leq y$ for every $y \in S$. It follows easily that if a nonempty set has a lower bound it has a greatest lower bound.

The property of Theorem 1 will be the only one used to obtain all further properties of the real numbers. Thus, the fact that R is an Archimedean ordered field in which every nonempty set with an upper bound has a least upper bound is basic to all further developments.

We shall always refer to the least upper bound of a set S as its **supremum,** and designate it as sup S. The greatest lower bound of S will be called its **infimum,** and designated as inf S.

EXERCISES

1.1 For every set A, show that $A = \mathscr{C}(\mathscr{C}A)$.

1.2 Show that if A is a subset of B and B is a subset of $\mathscr{C}$, then A is a subset of $\mathscr{C}$.

1.3 Show that $A \cup B$ is the unique set which contains A and B and is contained in every set which contains A and B.

1.4 Show that $A \cap B$ is the unique set which is contained in A and B and contains every set which is contained in A and B.

1.5 Show that $(A \cup B) \cup C = A \cup (B \cup C)$ and $A \cup B = B \cup A$.

1.6 Show that $(A \cap B) \cap C = A \cap (B \cap C)$ and $A \cap B = B \cap A$.

1.7 Show that $(A \cup B) \cap C = (A \cap C) \cup (B \cap C)$.

1.8 Show that $(A \cap B) \cup C = (A \cup C) \cap (B \cup C)$.

1.9 Generalize the statements of Exercises 1.7 and 1.8.

2.1 Show that if A has the same cardinal number as B then B has the same cardinal number as A.

2.2 Show that if A has the same cardinal number as B and B has the same cardinal number as C, then A has the same cardinal number as C.

2.3 Give an example of a mapping which is neither injective nor surjective.

2.4 Give an example of a mapping which is injective but not surjective.

2.5 Give an example of a mapping which is surjective but not injective.

2.6 Show that for any mappings f, g, and h,

$$(f \circ g) \circ h = f \circ (g \circ h).$$

3.1 Define an order relation for the set of all circles in the plane for which it is an ordered set.

3.2 Define an order relation for the set of polynomials for which it is an ordered set.

3.3 Show that axioms (*a*) and (*c*) for the natural numbers imply that every natural number has an immediate successor.

3.4 Show that a set is infinite if and only if it has the same cardinal number as a proper subset of itself.

3.5 Ordered sets are said to be isomorphic if there is an order-preserving bijective mapping between them. Show that any two ordered sets, which satisfy the axioms given in the text for natural numbers, are isomorphic.

3.6 If A, B, and C are ordered sets, A is isomorphic with B and B is isomorphic with C, show that A is isomorphic with C.

3.7 Show that every infinite set has a subset which has the same cardinal number as the set of natural numbers.

3.8 Show that if A and B are sets such that A has the same cardinal number as a subset of B and B has the same cardinal number as a subset of A, then A has the same cardinal number as B.

3.9 Give an example of ordered sets A and B such that A is isomorphic with an ordered subset of B, and B is isomorphic with an ordered subset of A, but A is not isomorphic with B. (The order in the ordered subset is always to be the same as that in the set itself.)

3.10 Give the details of the definition of addition for natural numbers.

3.11 Give the details of the definition of multiplication for natural numbers.

3.12 An ordered set is said to be of type η if
(a) it has the same cardinal number as the natural numbers,
(b) there is at least one element between any two of its elements,
(c) it has no last element and no first element.
Show that any two ordered sets of type η are isomorphic.

3.13 Using mathematical induction, find an expression for

$$1^2 + 2^2 + \cdots + n^2.$$

3.14 Using mathematical induction, show that

$$(1^3 + 2^3 + \cdots + n^3) = (1 + 2 + \cdots + n)^2.$$

3.15 Using mathematical induction, prove the binomial theorem

$$(a + b)^n = a^n + \frac{n!}{1!\,(n-1)!}\,a^{n-1}b + \frac{n!}{2!\,(n-2)!}\,a^{n-2}b^2 + \cdots + b^n.$$

3.16 Show that every subsequence of a subsequence of a given sequence is itself a subsequence of the given sequence.

4.1 Show that the axioms given for the rationals imply that $0 \cdot x = 0$, for every rational x.

4.2 Consider decimal expansions. Show that such an expansion represents a rational number if and only if it is repeating, i.e., of the form

$$n\,.\,a_1 \cdots a_r b_1 \cdots b_k b_1 \cdots b_k \cdots.$$

4.3 Show that if x is a rational number, $x \geq 0$, and $x < \frac{1}{n}$, for every n, then $x = 0$.

4.4 A set S is said to be countable if it has the same cardinal number as a subset of the natural numbers. Show that the union of a countable set of countable sets is countable.

4.5 Show that the set of rational numbers has the same cardinal number as the set of natural numbers.

5.1 If p is a prime number, show that there is no rational number x such that $x^2 = p$.

5.2 For every prime number p, show that for every $\epsilon > 0$ there are rational numbers x, y such that

$$x^2 < p < y^2 < x^2 + \epsilon.$$

5.3 Show that every ordered field has an ordered subfield isomorphic with the rationals.

6.1 Exhibit a bijective mapping between $(0, 1)$ and $[0, 1]$.

6.2 Show that if an ordered field is non-archimedean it has an open lower segment with no right end point.

6.3 Show that the real number system is not a proper subfield of any Archimedean ordered field.

6.4 Show that a proper ordered subfield of the real number system has an open lower segment with no right end point.

6.5 If $I \neq 0$, define $1/I$.

6.6 Give details showing that the reals constitute an Archimedean ordered field.

6.7 For every real x, define $|x|$ and show that for any x, y,

$$|x + y| \leq |x| + |y|.$$

6.8 For every real $x > 0$, and every natural number k, show that there is a real number y such that $y^k = x$. Then y is called the positive kth root of x.

CHAPTER 2

TOPOLOGY OF THE REALS

1. NESTED INTERVALS

An interval $I \subset \mathrm{R}$ is a set such that if $x, y \in I$, $x < y$, then $x < z < y$ implies $z \in I$.

By Theorem 1, every bounded interval I has a greatest lower bound, a, and a least upper bound, b, called the end points of I. If neither end point belongs to I, then I is called **open** and is designated as $I = (a, b)$. If both end points belong to I, then I is called **closed** and is designated as $I = [a, b]$. The **semiopen** cases $I = [a, b)$ and $I = (a, b]$ are also considered.

We recall that a sequence of real numbers is a mapping

$$f: N \to \mathrm{R}.$$

We use the customary notation $\{s_n\}$ or $s_1, s_2, \cdots, s_n, \cdots$, for a sequence.

A sequence $\{s_n\}$ is called a **null** sequence, or convergent to 0, if for every $\epsilon > 0$ there is an N such that $n > N$ implies $|s_n| < \epsilon$.

Example A The sequence $\{1/n\}$ is a null sequence.

Let $\epsilon > 0$. There is an N such that $1/N < \epsilon$. For every $n > N$, $1/n < 1/N < \epsilon$.

Example B If $0 < a < 1$, the sequence $\{a^n\}$ is a null sequence.

Let $b = 1/a$. Then $b > 1$ so that

$$b = 1 + h, \qquad h > 0.$$

By the binomial theorem,

$$b^n = (1 + h)^n > nh$$

for every n.

Let $\epsilon > 0$. There is an N such that $Nh > 1/\epsilon$. Then $n > N$ implies

$$b^n > Nh > \frac{1}{\epsilon},$$

so that

$$a^n = \frac{1}{b^n} < \epsilon.$$

If $I = [a, b]$, the length of I is the number

$$|I| = b - a.$$

A sequence $\{I_n\}$ of closed intervals is called **decreasing** if, for every $n = 1, 2, \cdots$,

$$I_{n+1} \subset I_n.$$

Let $\{I_n\}$ be a decreasing sequence of closed intervals. It is said to be **nested** if the sequence $\{|I_n|\}$ of lengths is null. In other words, the sequence $\{b_n - a_n\}$ is null, where $I_n = [a_n, b_n]$, $n = 1, 2, \cdots$.

Theorem 1

If $\{I_n\}$ is a nest of closed intervals, then $\bigcap_{n=1}^{\infty} I_n$ consists of exactly one point.

Proof

Let $I_n = [a_n, b_n]$, $n = 1, 2, \cdots$. Then, for every n,

$$a_n \leq a_{n+1} < b_{n+1} \leq b_n.$$

We first show that $a_n < b_m$ for every m and n. If $n < m$ then $a_n \leq a_m < b_m$. If $m < n$ then $a_n < b_n \leq b_m$.

Let S be the value set of $\{a_n\}$. Then each b_m is, by the last remark, an upper bound of S. In particular, S has an upper bound, so that it has a least upper bound u. Then $u \geq a_n$, for every n. Also, $u \leq b_n$ for every n. Thus $u \in I_n$ for every n. So, $u \in \bigcap_{n=1}^{\infty} I_n$. Let $x \neq u$. Since $\{b_n - a_n\}$ is a null sequence, there is an n such that $|x - u| > b_n - a_n$ so that $x \notin I_n$. ▮

A nest of open intervals may be defined similarly. The intersection of a nest of open intervals may be empty. For example, let $J_n = (0, 1/n)$, $n = 1, 2, \cdots$. Then $x \leq 0$ implies $x \notin J$, and $x > 0$ implies there is an n with $1/n < x$ so that $x \notin J_n$. Hence,

$$\bigcap_{n=1}^{\infty} J_n = \varnothing .$$

2. CONVERGENT SEQUENCES

A sequence $\{s_n\}$ is said to be a **Cauchy sequence** if for every $\epsilon > 0$ there is an N such that $m, n > N$ implies

$$|s_n - s_m| < \epsilon.$$

Thus, a sequence $\{s_n\}$ is Cauchy if and only if, for every $\epsilon > 0$, there is a closed interval I of length $|I| < \epsilon$ and an N such that $n > N$ implies $s_n \in I$. We leave the easy proof of this remark to the reader.

A sequence $\{s_n\}$ is said to **converge** to a number s if, for every $\epsilon > 0$ there is an N such that $n > N$ implies $|s - s_n| < \epsilon$.

If $\{s_n\}$ converges to s, we write

$$\lim_n s_n = s.$$

In particular, if $\{s_n\}$ is a null sequence then

$$\lim_n s_n = 0.$$

We first prove

Theorem 2

Every Cauchy sequence of reals converges.

Proof

Let $\{s_n\}$ be a Cauchy sequence. There is a closed interval I_1, with $|I_1| < 1$, and an N_1 such that $s_n \in I_1$ for every $n > N_1$. There is a closed interval I_2', with $|I_2'| < \frac{1}{2}$, and an N_2' such that $s_n \in I_2'$ for every $n > N_2'$. Let $I_2 = I_1 \cap I_2'$ and $N_2 = \max(N_1, N_2')$. Then $N_2 > N_1$, $I_2 \subset I_1$, $|I_2| < \frac{1}{2}$, and $s_n \in I_2$ for every $n > N_2$. By induction, we obtain $\{I_k\}$, $\{N_k\}$ such that

$$I_{k+1} \subset I_k, \qquad N_{k+1} > N_k, \qquad k = 1, 2, \cdots$$

and $|I_k| < 1/k$, with $s_n \in I_k$ for all $n > N_k$.

Then $\{I_k\}$, as a nest of closed intervals, has a single point s as its intersection.

We show that $\lim_n s_n = s$. Let $\epsilon > 0$. There is a k such that $|I_k| < \epsilon$. For every $n > N_k$, $s_n \in I_k$ so that, since $s \in I_k$,

$$|s - s_n| < \epsilon. \quad ∎$$

Remark For the same reason that in the rational numbers an open lower segment need not have a right end point, there are Cauchy sequences of rational numbers which do not converge.

We now list some simple properties of convergence sequences.

(a) Every convergent sequence is a Cauchy sequence.

Proof

Suppose $\{s_n\}$ is a sequence and $\lim_n s_n = s$. Let $\epsilon > 0$. There is an N such that $n > N$ implies $|s - s_n| < \epsilon/2$. Then n, $m > N$ implies $|s_n - s_m| \le |s - s_n| + |s - s_m| < (\epsilon/2) + (\epsilon/2) = \epsilon$. ∎

Remark This result holds for the rational numbers.

(b) If $\lim_n s_n = s$ and $\lim_n s_n = t$ then $s = t$ so that a sequence can converge to only one limit.

Proof

Let $\epsilon > 0$. There is an N_1 such that $n > N_1$ implies $|s - s_n| < \epsilon/2$ and an N_2 such that $n > N_2$ implies $|t - s_n| < \epsilon/2$. For $n > \max(N_1, N_2)$,

$$|s - t| \le |s - s_n| + |t - t_n| < \frac{\epsilon}{2} + \frac{\epsilon}{2} = \epsilon.$$

Since $|s - t| < \epsilon$, for every $\epsilon > 0$, we have $s = t$. ∎

(c) Every convergent sequence is bounded.

Proof

Suppose $\lim_n s_n = s$. There is an N such that $n > N$ implies $|s - s_n| < 1$, so that $|s_n| < |s| + 1$. Let

$$M = \max(|s_1|, \cdots, |s_N|, |s|) + 1.$$

Then $|s_n| < M$ for every $n = 1, 2, \cdots$. ∎

(d) If $\{s_n\}$ converges to s, then so does every subsequence of $\{s_n\}$.

We leave the proof to the reader.

(e) If $\{s_n\}$ converges to s and $a \in \mathrm{R}$, then $\{as_n\}$ converges to as.

Proof

The statement is obvious if $a = 0$. Suppose $a \neq 0$. Let $\epsilon > 0$. There is an N such that $|s - s_n| < \epsilon/|a|$, for every $n > N$. Then, for $n > N$,

$$|as - as_n| = |a|\,|s - s_n| < \epsilon. \quad \blacksquare$$

(f) If $\lim_n s_n = s$ and $\lim_n t_n = t$ then $\lim_n (s_n + t_n) = s + t$.

Proof

Let $\epsilon > 0$. There is an N_1 such that $n > N_1$ implies $|s - s_n| < \epsilon/2$, and an N_2 such that $n > N_2$ implies $|t - t_n| < \epsilon/2$. Let $N = \max(N_1, N_2)$. Then $n > N$ implies

$$|(s + t) - (s_n + t_n)| \leq |s - s_n| + |t - t_n| < \frac{\epsilon}{2} + \frac{\epsilon}{2} = \epsilon. \quad \blacksquare$$

(g) If $\lim_n s_n = s$ and $\lim_n t_n = t$ then $\lim_n s_n t_n = st$.

Proof

There is an M_1 such that $|s_n| < M_1$, for every n, and $|s| < M_1$, and an M_2 such that $|t_n| < M_2$, for every n, and $|t| < M_2$. Let $M = \max(M_1, M_2)$.

Let $\epsilon > 0$. There is an N_1 such that $n > N_1$ implies $|s - s_n| < \epsilon/2M$ and an N_2 such that $n > N_2$ implies $|t - t_n| < \epsilon/2M$. Let $N = \max(N_1, N_2)$. Then $n > N$ implies

$$\begin{aligned} |st - s_n t_n| &= |st - s_n t + s_n t - s_n t_n| \\ &\leq |t|\,|s - s_n| + |s_n|\,|t - t_n| \\ &< M \cdot \frac{\epsilon}{2M} + M \cdot \frac{\epsilon}{2M} = \epsilon. \quad \blacksquare \end{aligned}$$

(h) If $s_n \neq 0$, for every n, and $\lim s_n = s \neq 0$, there is a $k > 0$ such that $|s_n| > k$ for all n.

We leave the proof to the reader.

(i) If $\lim_n s_n = s$, $t_n \neq 0$ for every n, and $\lim_n t_n = t \neq 0$, then

$$\lim_n \frac{s_n}{t_n} = \frac{s}{t}.$$

Proof

There is a $k > 0$ such that $|t_n| > k$, for every n, and $|t| > k$. There is an M such that $|s_n| < M$ for every n. Let $\epsilon > 0$. There is an N such that $n > N$ implies $|s - s_n| < \epsilon k/2$, and $|t - t_n| < \epsilon k^2/2M$. Then $n > N$ implies

$$\left|\frac{s}{t} - \frac{s_n}{t_n}\right| = \frac{|st_n - s_n t|}{|tt_n|} = \frac{|st_n - s_n t_n + s_n t_n - s_n t|}{|tt_n|}$$

$$\leq \frac{|s - s_n|}{|t|} + \frac{|s_n|\,|t - t_n|}{|tt_n|} < \frac{\epsilon k}{2k} + \frac{\epsilon M k^2}{2Mk^2} = \epsilon. \quad \blacksquare$$

We add the following interesting fact.

(j) If $\lim_n s_n = s$ and $\sigma_n = \frac{1}{n}(s_1 + \cdots + s_n)$, $n = 1, 2, \cdots$, then $\{\sigma_n\}$ converges and $\lim_n \sigma_n = s$.

Proof

For every n,

$$|s - \sigma_n| = \left|s - \frac{1}{n}(s_1 + \cdots + s_n)\right| = \left|\frac{ns - (s_1 + \cdots + s_n)}{n}\right|$$

$$= \left|\frac{[ks + (n - k)s - (s_1 + \cdots + s_n)]}{n}\right|,$$

for every $k < n$. So

$$|s - \sigma_n| \leq \frac{|ks - (s_1 + \cdots + s_k)|}{n} + \sum_{i=k+1}^{n} \frac{|s - s_i|}{n}.$$

Let $\epsilon > 0$. Choose k so large that $i > k$ implies $|s - s_i| < \epsilon/2$. Then, for every $n > k$,

$$\sum_{i=k+1}^{n} \frac{|s - s_i|}{n} < \frac{(n - k)\epsilon}{2n} < \frac{\epsilon}{2}.$$

So, for every $n > k$,

$$|s - \sigma_n| \leq \frac{|ks - (s_1 + \cdots + s_k)|}{n} + \frac{\epsilon}{2}.$$

But $|ks - (s_1 + \cdots + s_k)|$ is constant so that $\{|ks - (s_1 + \cdots + s_k)|/n\}$ is a null sequence. Hence, there is an $N > k$ such that $n > N$ implies $|ks - (s_1 + \cdots + s_k)|/n < \epsilon/2$, and $|s - \sigma_n| < \epsilon$.

Remark The sequence 0, 1, 0, 1, $\cdots$ does not converge but the corresponding sequence $\{\sigma_n\}$ converges to 1/2.

We give some examples of convergent sequences.

Example A For every $a > 0$, the sequence $\{a^{1/n}\}$ converges to 1.

Suppose $a > 1$. Then $a^{1/n} > 1$ for every n. Let $a^{1/n} = 1 + b_n$, $n = 1, 2, \cdots$. Then $b_n > 0$. Raising to the nth power, we obtain

$$a = (1 + b_n)^n > nb_n.$$

Then

$$b_n < \frac{a}{n}$$

and $\{b_n\}$ is a null sequence. It follows that $\lim_n a^{1/n} = 1$.

We leave the case $0 < a \leq 1$ to the reader.

Theorem 3

Every nondecreasing bounded sequence converges.

Proof

Let $\{s_n\}$ be a nondecreasing bounded sequence. Then $s_{n+1} \geq s_n$, $n = 1, 2, \cdots$, and there is a u such that $u > s_n$ for every n. Let $l < s_1$.

Let $\epsilon > 0$. There is an m such that $l + m\epsilon > u$. It follows that there is a k such that $l + k\epsilon < s_N$ for some N but $l + (k + 1)\epsilon \geq s_n$ for every n. Thus $n, m > N$ implies $|s_n - s_m| < \epsilon$. Thus $\{s_n\}$ is a Cauchy sequence so that it converges. ∎

Example B The sequence $\{(1 + (1/n))^n\}$ converges.

We prove that the sequence is nondecreasing and that 3 is an upper bound.

(a) For every n, $\left(1 + \frac{1}{n+1}\right)^{n+1} > \left(1 + \frac{1}{n}\right)^n$.

By the binomial theorem,

$$\left(1 + \frac{1}{n}\right)^n = 1 + 1 + \frac{1}{2!}\frac{n-1}{n} + \frac{1}{3!}\frac{n-1}{n}\frac{n-2}{n} + \cdots$$

where there are $n + 1$ terms, and

$$\left(1 + \frac{1}{n+1}\right)^{n+1} = 1 + 1 + \frac{1}{2!}\frac{n}{n+1} + \frac{1}{3!}\frac{n}{n+1}\frac{n-1}{n+1} + \cdots$$

where there are $n + 2$ terms.

Since $k/n < (k+1)/(n+1)$, for all $k = 1, \cdots, n-1$, it follows that each term, after the first 2, in the expansion of $\left(1 + \frac{1}{n+1}\right)^{n+1}$ exceeds the corresponding term in the expansion of $\left(1 + \frac{1}{n}\right)^{n}$. Moreover, there is a positive term left over in the expansion of $\left(1 + \frac{1}{n+1}\right)^{n+1}$. Hence

$$\left(1 + \frac{1}{n+1}\right)^{n+1} > \left(1 + \frac{1}{n}\right)^{n}.$$

(b) For every n,

$$\left(1 + \frac{1}{n}\right)^{n} < 3.$$

It is clear that

$$\begin{aligned}\left(1 + \frac{1}{n}\right)^{n} &< 1 + 1 + \frac{1}{2!} + \frac{1}{3!} + \cdots + \frac{1}{n!} \\ &< 1 + 1 + \frac{1}{2} + \frac{1}{2^2} + \cdots + \frac{1}{2^{n-1}} \\ &= 3 - \frac{1}{2^{n-1}} < 3.\end{aligned}$$

By **(a)** and **(b)**, $\{(1 + 1/n)^n\}$ converges. We now make a more precise statement regarding the limit of this sequence, which is a very important number, the natural base for logarithms, e. Fix n. For every $m > n$,

$$\left(1 + \frac{1}{m}\right)^{m} > 1 + 1 + \frac{1}{2!}\,\frac{m-1}{m} + \cdots + \frac{1}{n!}\,\frac{(m-1)\cdots(m-n+1)}{m^{n-1}}.$$

The right hand side converges to $1 + 1 + 1/2! + 1/n!$ as m increases and the left hand side converges to e. Hence

$$e \geq 1 + 1 + \frac{1}{2!} + \cdots + \frac{1}{n!}$$

for every n.

On the other hand

$$\begin{aligned}\left(1 + \frac{1}{m}\right)^{m} &< 1 + 1 + \frac{1}{2!} + \cdots + \frac{1}{n!} + \frac{1}{2^n} + \cdots + \frac{1}{2^m} \\ &< 1 + 1 + \frac{1}{2!} + \cdots + \frac{1}{n!} + \frac{1}{2^{n-1}}\end{aligned}$$

so that

$$e \leq 1 + 1 + \frac{1}{2!} + \cdots + \frac{1}{n!} + \frac{1}{2^{n-1}}$$

for every n.

Thus

$$\left| e - \left(1 + 1 + \frac{1}{2!} + \cdots + \frac{1}{n!}\right) \right| \leq \frac{1}{2^{n-1}},$$

for every n. We may use this to write e to as many decimals as we please.

Later, we shall use the above expression to prove that e is irrational.

3. BOLZANO-WEIERSTRASS THEOREM

We first give this theorem for sequences.

Theorem 4

If $\{s_n\}$ is a bounded sequence then $\{s_n\}$ has a convergent subsequence.

Proof

Since $\{s_n\}$ is bounded, there is a closed interval $I_0 = [a, b]$ such that $s_n \in I_0$ for every n. If we let

$$I_1^1 = \left[a, a + \frac{b-a}{2}\right], \qquad I_1^2 = \left[a + \frac{b-a}{2}, b\right],$$

then at least one of these intervals contains s_n for infinitely many values of n. Let I_1 be such an interval. By induction, we obtain a decreasing sequence

$$I_0 \supset I_1 \supset \cdots \supset I_n \supset \cdots$$

of closed intervals, each of length one half that of its immediate predecessor, each of which contains s_n for infinitely many values of n.

Let x be the unique point in all the I_n. Let $s_{n_1} \in I_1$. Since I_2 contains s_n for infinitely many values of n, there is an $n_2 > n_1$ such that $s_{n_2} \in I_2$. By induction we obtain

$$n_1 < n_2 < \cdots < n_k < \cdots$$

such that $s_{n_k} \in I_k$, $k = 1, \cdots, n, \cdots$.

We show that $\{s_{n_k}\}$ converges to x. Let $\epsilon > 0$. There is a k such that $|I_k| < \epsilon$. Then for $j > k$, $s_{n_j} \in I_k$ so that $|x - s_{n_j}| < \epsilon$. ∎

This theorem has an analogous version in terms of sets rather than sequences. For this purpose we need to define a limit point of a set.

Let $S \subset R$ be a set. A point x is called a **limit point** of S if for every open interval J, with $x \in J$, the set $S \cap J$ is infinite.

For example,

(a) If S has the numbers $1/2, 1/3, \cdots, 1/n, \cdots$ as its elements, then 0 is a limit point of S and the only limit point of S.

(b) If S is finite then it has no limit points.

(c) If S is the set of rational numbers, then every real number is a limit point of S.

(d) If S is a closed interval, then the limit points of S are precisely the points of S.

Theorem 4'

If S is a bounded infinite set, then S has at least one limit point.

Proof

Since S is bounded, there is a closed interval $I_0 = [a, b]$ such that $S \subset I_0$. Let $I_1^1 = [a, a + (b - a)/2]$ and $I_1^2 = [a + (b - a)/2, b]$. Then at least one of the sets $I_1^1 \cap S$ or $I_1^2 \cap S$ is infinite. Let I_1 be one of the sets I_1^1 or I_1^2 whose intersection with S is infinite. Proceeding by induction, we obtain a decreasing sequence

$$I_0 \supset I_1 \supset \cdots \supset I_n \supset \cdots$$

of closed intervals, each of length one half that of its immediate predecessor for each of which the intersection with S is infinite. Let x be the unique point in $\bigcap_{n=1}^{\infty} I_n$. Now, let J be any open interval with $x \in J$. Then $J = (\alpha, \beta)$ where $\alpha < x < \beta$. There is an n such that $|I_n| < \min(x - \alpha, \beta - x)$. Then $S \cap I_n \subset S \cap J$ is infinite. x is accordingly a limit point of S. ∎

4. BOREL COVERING THEOREM

A set S is said to be *covered* by a collection $\mathscr{T}$ of sets if every $x \in S$ is in some $T \in \mathscr{T}$.

The following theorem will be used frequently in this book.

Theorem 5

If $I = [a, b]$ is a closed interval and $\mathscr{J}$ is a collection of open intervals which covers I, then a finite number of the intervals in $\mathscr{J}$ covers I.

Proof

Let $x \in S$ if $[a, x]$ is covered by a finite number of the intervals in $\mathscr{J}$. Then S is nonempty, and if $x \in S$ and $a < y < x$ then $y \in S$. Suppose the greatest lower bound of S is $x < b$. But there is a $J \in \mathscr{J}$ such that $x \in J$. Let $y \in J$, $y < x$. Then $[a, y]$ is covered by a finite set $J_1, \cdots, J_n$ of intervals of $\mathscr{J}$. Let $z > x$, $z \in J$. Then $[a, z]$ is covered by $J_1, \cdots, J_n, J$ so that $z \in S$ contradicting the assumption that x is an upper bound of S. ∎

Let $\{s_n\}$ be a bounded sequence, and let S be the set of all limits of convergent subsequences of $\{s_n\}$. Then S is a bounded set. Let

$$u = \sup S.$$

There is a convergent subsequence of $\{s_n\}$ whose limit exceeds $u - 1$. There is thus an n_1 such that $s_{n_1} > u - 1$. There is a convergent subsequence of $\{s_n\}$ whose limit exceeds $u - 1/2$. There is thus an $n_2 > n_1$ such that $s_{n_2} > u - 1/2$. In this way, we obtain an increasing sequence

$$n_1 > n_2 > \cdots > n_k > \cdots$$

of natural numbers, such that

$$\lim_k s_{n_k} = u.$$

The number u is then the maximum of the set of limits of convergent subsequences of $\{s_n\}$. It is designated as

$$\limsup_n s_n.$$

The number $\liminf_n s_n$ is defined in similar fashion.

5. CLOSED AND OPEN SETS

Open intervals are a special case of an important class of sets called open sets. A set $G \subset R$ is **open** if every $x \in G$ is in an open interval J such that $J \subset G$.

As examples of open sets we have:

(a) Every open interval is an open set.
(b) Every set which is the union of open intervals is open.
(c) If G_u is an open set for every $u \in U$, then $G = \bigcup[G_u\colon u \in U]$ is open.

Proof

Let $x \in G$. Then $x \in G_u$ for some u. There is an open interval J such that $x \in J$ and $J \subset G_u \subset G$. Hence G is open. ∎

(d) If G and H are open then $G \cap H$ is open.

Proof

Let $x \in G \cap H$. There is an open interval J_1 such that $x \in J_1$ and $J_1 \subset G$, and there is an open interval J_2 such that $x \in J_2$ and $J_2 \subset H$. Now $J = J_1 \cap J_2$ is an open interval, $x \in J$ and $J \subset G \cap H$. Hence $G \cap H$ is open. ∎

(e) It follows by induction that the intersection of a finite number of open sets is open. However, the intersection of an infinite number of open sets need not be open. For example, let $G_n = (-1/n, 1/n)$, $n = 1, 2, \cdots$. Then $\bigcap_{n=1}^{\infty} G_n$ is the set which has one point, 0, and so is not open.

We shall give a theorem which describes the structure of every open set. For this theorem, we need some preliminaries. A set S is said to be **countable** if there is an injective-mapping of S into N. An example of a nontrivial countable set is the set Q of rationals. We leave the proof of this for the reader. In passing, we prove that

R is not countable.

Proof

Let $S \subset$ R be countable. It suffices to show that $S \neq$ R. S may be put into one-one correspondence with N so that its elements may be labeled

$$a_1, a_2, \cdots, a_n, \cdots.$$

Let I_1 be a closed interval of length less than 1 such that $a_1 \notin I_1$. Let $I_2 \subset I_1$ be of length less than 1/2 such that $a_2 \notin I_2$. In this way, obtain a nest $\{I_n\}$ of closed intervals such that, for every n, $a_n \notin I_n$. Let x be the unique point in all the I_n. For every n, $x \in I_n$ and $a_n \notin I_n$ so that $x \neq a_n$. Hence, $x \notin S$. ∎

Theorem 6

If $G \subset$ R is open, then G is the union of a countable number of pairwise disjoint open intervals.

Proof

Suppose G nonempty. Let $x \in G$. Let $U = [y\colon (x, y) \subset G]$. Since there is an open interval I, with $x \in I$ and $I \subset G$, it follows that U is nonempty. If U has an upper bound, let b_x be the least upper bound. Then $(x, b_x) \subset G$. If U does not have an upper bound then every point to the right of x is in G. Similarly, either every point to the left of x is in G or there is a greatest lower bound a_x of the set L of numbers, y, such that $(y, x) \subset G$. We then obtain an interval $J_x = (a_x, b_x)$, which may be unbounded, such that $x \in J_x$ and $J_x \subset G$.

We show that, for $x, y \in G$, either $J_x = J_y$ or $J_x \cap J_y = \varnothing$. Suppose $J_x \cap J_y \neq \varnothing$ and $J_x \neq J_y$. Then $J_x \cup J_y$ is an open interval which contains J_x as a proper subset. Then there is either a $z \in U$, $z > b_x$ or a $w \in L$, $w < a_x$. In either case, the assumption that $J_x \neq J_y$ is contradicted. It follows that G is the union of pairwise disjoint open intervals. That these open intervals are countable in number follows since every open interval contains a rational number. We thus obtain an injective-mapping of our set of intervals into the rationals, which makes them countable in number. ∎

A set S is said to be **closed** if it is the complement of an open set.

We list some simple properties of closed sets.

(a) S is closed if and only if it contains all its limit points.

Proof

Suppose S is closed. Then $T = \mathscr{C}S$ is open. Let $x \in T$. There is an open interval J with $x \in J$ and $J \subset T$. So $J \cap S$ is empty and x is not a limit point of S.

Suppose S contains all its limit points. Let $x \in T = \mathscr{C}S$. There is an open interval J such that $x \in J$ and $J \cap S$ is finite, say $S = \{x_1, \cdots, x_n\}$ all different from x. Let $d = \min(|x - x_1|, \cdots, |x - x_n|)$. The open interval $I = (x - d, x + d)$ is such that $x \in I$ and $I \subset T$. Hence T is open and S is closed. ∎

(b) The intersection of any number of closed sets is closed. We leave the proof to the reader.

(c) The union of two closed sets is closed. We leave the proof to the reader.

Associated with every set S is a closed set $\bar{S}$ called the closure of S. The **closure** $\bar{S}$ of S is the intersection of all closed sets containing S.

(d) A point $x \in \bar{S}$ if and only if $x \in S$ or x is a limit point of S.

Proof

Every limit point of S is also a limit point of $\bar{S}$. Hence $\bar{S}$ contains S together with all its limit points. It remains only to show that the set T composed of S together with all its limit points is closed. Let $x \in \mathscr{C}T$. Then x is in an open interval $J \subset \mathscr{C}T$. Thus $\mathscr{C}T$ is open. ∎

We give some properties of $\bar{S}$.

(a) For every S, $\bar{S} \supset S$.
(b) For every S, T, $\overline{S \cup T} = \bar{S} \cup \bar{T}$.
(c) For every S, $\bar{S} = \bar{\bar{S}}$.

We leave the proofs to the reader.

Finally, we give some examples of closed sets.

(a) Every closed interval is a closed set.
(b) Every finite union of closed intervals is a closed set.
(c) The set whose elements are

$$0, 1, \frac{1}{2}, \cdots, \frac{1}{n}, \cdots$$

is a closed set.
(d) The set of rational numbers is neither open nor closed.

Theorem 7

The only subsets of R *which are both open and closed are* R *itself and the empty set* $\varnothing$.

Proof

It is clear that R and $\varnothing$ are both open and closed. Let G be an open set that is neither R nor $\varnothing$. Then one of the open intervals J of G in the structure theorem, Theorem 6, has an end point x. Now, $x \notin G$. But x is a limit point of G so that G is not closed. ∎

We now extend the nested interval theorem, the Bolzano-Weierstrass theorem, and the Borel covering theorem to bounded closed sets.

We first prove

Lemma 1

If F is a closed set, and $\{s_n\}$ is a convergent sequence with values in F, then $s = \lim_n s_n \in F$.

Proof

We may suppose $s_n \neq s$, $n = 1, 2, \cdots$ for, otherwise, $s = s_n \in F$ already.

Then every open interval J containing s must contain s_n for infinitely many values of n (and of s_n). Thus, s is a limit point of F and is accordingly in F. ∎

Theorem 8

If $\{F_n\}$ is a decreasing sequence of nonempty bounded closed sets, then

$$F = \bigcap_{n=1}^{\infty} F_n$$

is nonempty.

Proof

There is a closed interval I such that $F_1 \subset I$. For every n, let $x_n \in F_n$. Then, $\{x_n\}$ is a bounded sequence, so that it has a convergent subsequence $\{x_{n_k}\}$, which converges to $x \in I$. For every n, there is a k_0 such that $k > k_0$ implies $x_{n_k} \in F_n$. By Lemma 1, $x \in F_n$. Since $x \in F_n$ for every n, it follows that $x \in F$.

Theorem 9

If F is a closed bounded set, then every infinite $S \subset F$ has a limit point in F.

Proof

We leave the proof of this theorem, which is very much like that of Theorem 4, to the reader. ∎

Theorem 10

Let F be a closed bounded set, and $\mathscr{G}$ a family of open sets which covers F. Then, a finite number of sets in $\mathscr{G}$ covers F.

Proof

It follows from the fact that F is closed and bounded that it contains both its greatest lower bound l and its least upper bound u. Let $x \in X$ if and only if $x \in F$ and $F \cap [l, x]$ may be covered by a finite number of sets in $\mathscr{G}$. The least upper bound of S is in S. Let it be b. We show that $b = u$. If $b < u$, and every open interval containing b contains points of F to right of b, there is a member of $\mathscr{G}$ that contains b and points of F to the right of b, so that there is an $x \in S$, $x > b$. Otherwise, the part of F to the right of b has a smallest element c which is in a member of $\mathscr{G}$. It follows that $c \in S$. Thus the assumption that $b < u$ leads to a contradiction. ∎

EXERCISES

1.1 Show that the intersection of a sequence of closed intervals is either the empty set, a single point, or a closed interval.

1.2 Show that the intersection of a sequence of open intervals is either the empty set, a single point, a closed interval, an open interval, or a semi-open interval.

2.1 Show that a sequence $\{s_n\}$ is a Cauchy sequence if and only if, for every $\epsilon > 0$, there is an interval I, of length $|I| < \epsilon$, and an N such that $n > N$ implies $s_n \in I$.

2.2 For every bounded $\{s_n\}$ and $\{t_n\}$, show that

$$\limsup_n (s_n + t_n) \leq \limsup_n s_n + \limsup_n t_n.$$

2.3 Show that

$$\limsup_n s_n t_n \leq \limsup_n s_n \limsup_n t_n.$$

2.4 For every bounded $\{s_n\}$, for every n, let

$$u_n = \sup \{s_n, s_{n+1}, \cdots\}.$$

Show that $\{u_n\}$ is monotonically nonincreasing and that $\lim_n u_n = \limsup_n s_n$.

2.5 If s_n is an increasing sequence of positive numbers, show that the sequence $\{(s_1 + \cdots + s_n)/n\}$ is increasing.

2.6 Let $a > 0$, $s_1 > 0$, and for every n, let $s_{n+1} = (s_n + a)^{1/2}$. Discuss the convergence of $\{s_n\}$.

2.7 For any sequence $\{s_n\}$ show that $\limsup_n \dfrac{s_1 + \cdots + s_n}{n} \leq \limsup_n s_n$.

2.8 The set of limit points of a sequence $\{s_n\}$ is the set of limits of convergent subsequences of $\{s_n\}$. Show that for every closed set S, there is a sequence whose set of limit points is S.

2.9 If $\{s_n\}$ converges to s show that every subsequence of $\{s_n\}$ converges to s.

2.10 If $\{s_n\}$ converges to s, show that $\{\sigma_n\}$ converges to s, where

$$\sigma_n = \frac{1}{2^n} s_1 + \frac{1}{2^{n-1}} s_2 + \cdots + \frac{1}{2} s_n, \qquad n = 1, 2, \cdots.$$

2.11 Show that $\lim_n (\sqrt{n^2 + n} - n) = \dfrac{1}{2}$.

2.12 For any real a, show that

$$\lim_n (\sqrt{n^2 + a} - n) = 0.$$

2.13 For every $a > 0$, show that

$$\lim_n \frac{a^n}{n!} = 0.$$

3.1 Show that every bounded infinite set has a maximum limit point and a minimum limit point.

5.1 For any set S, let S' be the set of limit points of S. Show that S' is closed.

5.2 Give an example of a nonempty set for which $S' = S$.

5.3 Give an example of a nonempty set, which contains no intervals, but for which $S' = S$.

5.4 Show that every uncountable set of real numbers has at least one limit point.

5.5 If S is nonempty, and $S' = S$, show that S is uncountable.

5.6 A set S is said to be isolated, if $S' \cap S$ is empty. Show that every isolated set is countable.

5.7 A set S is said to be semi-isolated if every $x \in S$ is the end point of an open interval whose intersection with S is empty. Show that every semi-isolated set is countable.

5.8 For every S and T, show that

$$\overline{S \cup T} = \bar{S} \cup \bar{T}.$$

5.9 Let S be a set in the plane. A point in the plane will be called a **singular** point of S if it is a limit point of S but is the vertex of an angle greater than 180° which has no point of S in its interior. Show that the set of singular points of S is countable for any set S.

5.10 Show that the union of two closed sets is closed.

5.11 Show that the union of countably many closed sets need not be closed.

5.12 Show that the set of rational numbers is neither open nor closed.

5.13 Show that there is a bijective mapping between the set of all closed sets and the set of all real numbers.

5.14 If S is an uncountable set of positive real numbers, show that for every M, there is a finite subset of S whose sum is greater than M.

CHAPTER 3

INFINITE SERIES

1. SUM OF A SERIES

It is important to know what is meant by the sum of an infinite series. For an infinite sequence, $\{a_n\}$, we consider the expression

$$a_1 + a_2 + \cdots + a_n + \cdots.$$

Such an expression is called an **infinite series.** The summands $a_1, a_2, \cdots a_n, \cdots$ are called the **terms** of the series. The theory of summation of series is referred to that of convergence of sequences.

For this purpose we associate with a series its **sequence of partial sums.** For the above series the sequence $\{s_n\}$ of partial sums is defined by

$$s_1 = a_1, \qquad s_2 = a_1 + a_2, \cdots, \qquad s_n = a_1 + a_2 + \cdots + a_n + \cdots.$$

Example A Consider the infinite series

$$\frac{1}{2} + \frac{1}{4} + \frac{1}{8} + \cdots + \frac{1}{2^n} + \cdots.$$

The associated sequence of partial sums is

$$1/2, 3/4, 7/8, \cdots, (2^n - 1)/2^n, \cdots.$$

Example B Consider the infinite series

$$1 - 1 + 1 - 1 + \cdots.$$

The associated sequence of partial sums is 1, 0, 1, 0, $\cdots$.

A series $a_1 + a_2 + \cdots + a_n + \cdots$ is said to **converge** if its associated sequence $s_1 = a_1$, $s_2 = a_1 + a_2, \cdots$, $s_n = a_1 + a_2 + \cdots + a_n$, $\cdots$ converges. The **sum** of the series is then defined to be the number $s = \lim_n s_n$. A series is said to **diverge** if its associated sequence of partial sums diverges (does not converge).

In Example A, the series converges to 1. In Example B, the series diverges.

We state a simple but important fact. If $a_1 + a_2 + \cdots + a_n + \cdots$ converges, then $\{a_n\}$ is a null sequence.

Proof

Suppose $\{a_n\}$ is not a null sequence. Then, there is a $k > 0$ such that for every N there is an $n > N$ with $|a_n| > k$. For the associated sequence $\{s_n\}$ of partial sums, since $a_n = s_n - s_{n-1}$, for every n, it follows that for every N there is an $n \geq N$ with $|s_n - s_{n-1}| > k$. Hence, this sequence diverges. ∎

The converse is false, a fact which makes the theory of convergent series difficult.

Example C The series $1 + 1/2 + 1/3 + \cdots + 1/n + \cdots$ diverges even though its terms are a null sequence.

Let

$$s_n = 1 + \frac{1}{2} + \frac{1}{3} + \cdots + \frac{1}{n}.$$

Then

$$s_{2^n} > \frac{n}{2}.$$

It follows that $\{s_n\}$ diverges.

A sequence of real numbers converges if and only if it is a Cauchy sequence. We translate this fact to yield a criterion for convergence of series.

Theorem 1

A series $a_1 + a_2 + \cdots + a_n + \cdots$ converges if and only if, for every $\epsilon > 0$, there is an N such that for every $n > N$ and $p > 0$,

$$|a_{n+1} + \cdots + a_{n+p}| < \epsilon.$$

Proof

Let $\{s_n\}$ be the sequence of partial sums associated with the series. Let $\epsilon > 0$. Suppose $\{s_n\}$ converges. There is an N such that for every $n > N$ and $p > 0$, $|s_{n+p} - s_n| < \epsilon$; in other words

$$|a_{n+1} + \cdots + a_{n+p}| < \epsilon.$$

Conversely, suppose for every $\epsilon > 0$, there is an N such that $n > N$ and $p > 0$ implies $|a_{n+1} + \cdots + a_{n+p}| < \epsilon$. Then for every $n > N$ and $p > 0$, $|s_n - s_{n+p}| < \epsilon$. Or, for every $n, m > N$, $|s_n - s_m| < \epsilon$, so that $\{s_n\}$ converges. ∎

2. SERIES OF POSITIVE TERMS

We consider the case of an infinite series $a_1 + a_2 + \cdots + a_n + \cdots$, where $a_n > 0$, $n = 1, 2, \cdots$. For this case, the sequence $\{s_n\}$ of partial sums converges if and only if it is bounded.

As a first example, we consider a geometric series

$$a + ar + ar^2 + \cdots + ar^n + \cdots$$

where $a > 0$ and $r > 0$. We prove that such a series converges if $r < 1$ and diverges if $r \geq 1$.

Suppose $r \geq 1$. The sequence $\{ar^n\}$ is increasing so that it is not a null sequence. Hence, the series $a + ar + \cdots + ar^n + \cdots$ diverges.

Suppose $r < 1$. Then

$$s_n = a + ar + \cdots + ar^{n-1}$$

and

$$rs_n = ar + ar^2 + \cdots + ar^{n-1} + ar^n.$$

By subtraction,

$$s_n = \frac{a(1 - r^n)}{1 - r}.$$

Since $\{r^n\}$ is a null sequence, $\lim_n s_n = a/(1 - r)$. We have thus not only shown that the series converges but have found its sum.

An important method for showing that a given series converges or diverges is by comparing it with a series which is known to converge or diverge.

Comparison Test If $a_1 + a_2 + \cdots + a_n + \cdots$ is a convergent series of positive terms, $b_1 + b_2 + \cdots + b_n + \cdots$ is a series of positive terms, and there is an $M > 0$ such that $b_n < Ma_n$ for every n, then the series $b_1 + b_2 + \cdots + b_n + \cdots$ converges.

If $a_1 + a_2 + \cdots + a_n + \cdots$ is a divergent series of positive terms, $b_1 + b_2 + \cdots + b_n + \cdots$ is a series of positive terms, and there is an $M > 0$ such that $b_n > Ma_n$ for every n, then the series $b_1 + b_2 + \cdots + b_n + \cdots$ diverges.

Proof

In the first case, let $\{s_n\}$ be the sequence of partial sums of $a_1 + a_2 + \cdots + a_n + \cdots$ and $\{t_n\}$ the sequence of partial sums of $b_1 + b_2 + \cdots + b_n + \cdots$. Then $\{s_n\}$ is increasing and converges to s. For every n, $t_n \leq Ms_n < Ms$. Hence $\{t_n\}$ is bounded and, so, is convergent.

In the second case the sequence $\{s_n\}$ is unbounded. Since $t_n \geq Ms_n$, for every n, $\{t_n\}$ is also unbounded so that it diverges. ∎

If there were a single convergent series, which served as a comparison for all convergent series of positive terms, the theory would be complete and rather trivial. We now show that such a series does not exist. For this purpose, we introduce the idea of more slowly convergent series.

A convergent series $b_1 + b_2 + \cdots + b_n + \cdots$ of positive terms is said to converge more slowly than a series $a_1 + a_2 + \cdots + a_n + \cdots$ of positive terms if $\lim_n b_n/a_n = +\infty$, i.e., if for every M there is an N such that $n > N$ implies $b_n/a_n > M$.

Theorem 2

For every convergent series of positive terms there is a more slowly convergent series of positive terms.

Proof

Let $a_1 + a_2 + \cdots + a_n + \cdots$ be a convergent series whose sum is s. Then, for every $\epsilon > 0$, there is an n such that $|a_1 + \cdots + a_n - s| < \epsilon$. There is then an increasing sequence

$$n_1 < n_2 < \cdots < n_k < \cdots$$

such that, for every k,

$$|a_1 + \cdots + a_{n_k} - s| < \frac{1}{k \cdot 2^k}.$$

Now, for every n for which $n_k + 1 < n \leq n_{k+1}$ let $b_n = ka_n$. Let $b_n = a_n$ for $n \leq n_1$. Since, as is apparent, $a_{n_k+1} + \cdots + a_{n_{k+1}} < 1/(k \cdot 2^k)$, it follows that $b_{n_k+1} + \cdots + b_{n_{k+1}} < 1/2^k$. It follows easily that the series $b_1 + b_2 + \cdots + b_n + \cdots$ converges. It is also clear that $\lim_n b_n/a_n = +\infty$.

We make a digression and show that e is irrational. We showed that

$$\left| e - \left(1 + 1 + \frac{1}{2!} + \cdots + \frac{1}{n!}\right) \right| < \frac{1}{2^{n-1}}$$

for every n, so that the series

$$1 + 1 + \frac{1}{2!} + \cdots + \frac{1}{n!} + \cdots$$

converges to e. We show that for every n, $n!\,e$ is not an integer. Then ne is not an integer, so that e is irrational.

Now, $n!\left(1 + 1 + \frac{1}{2!} + \cdots + \frac{1}{n!}\right)$ is an integer, and so we need only show that $n!\left(\frac{1}{(n+1)!} + \frac{1}{(n+2)!} + \cdots\right) < 1$, i.e., $\frac{1}{n+1} + \frac{1}{(n+1)(n+2)} + \cdots < 1$. But,

$$\frac{1}{(n+1)} + \frac{1}{(n+1)(n+2)} + \cdots \leq \frac{1}{2} + \frac{1}{2 \cdot 3} + \cdots$$
$$< \frac{1}{2} + \frac{1}{2^2} + \cdots = 1.$$

This proves that e is irrational.

We return to a discussion of tests for convergence of series of positive terms.

Root Test If $a_1 + a_2 + \cdots + a_n + \cdots$ is a series of positive terms, then if there is an N and a $k < 1$ such that $a_n^{1/n} < k$ for every $n > N$, the series converges. If $a_n^{1/n} \geq 1$ for infinitely many values of n, then the series diverges.

Proof

The second statement is obvious. In order to prove the first statement, we note that $a_n < k^n$ for every $n > N$ so that the convergence follows by comparison with the geometric series. ∎

Another simple test which follows from the geometric series is the

Ratio Test If $a_1 + a_2 + \cdots + a_n + \cdots$ is a series of positive terms and there is an N and a $k < 1$ such that $a_{n+1}/a_n < k$ for all $n > N$, then the series converges.

Proof

We compare our series,

$$a_1 + a_2 + \cdots + a_N + \cdots + a_n + \cdots,$$

with the series

$$a_1 + a_2 + \cdots + a_N + a_N k + a_N k^2 + \cdots,$$

and the result follows. ∎

The statement which may be made here concerning divergent series is uninteresting.

Integral Test Although a careful discussion of integration will not be given until later, we shall make use of the integral of a decreasing function. This involves formalities which the reader knows from elementary mathematics.

Suppose f is defined for all $x > a$, where $a \geq 0$, and that f is a positive decreasing function, i.e., $x > y$ implies $f(x) < f(y)$. Then, the integral of f is said to be **convergent** if

$$\lim_n \int_a^n f < +\infty,$$

and it is said to be **divergent** if

$$\lim_n \int_a^n f = +\infty.$$

Let $a_1 + a_2 + \cdots + a_n + \cdots$ be a series whose terms form a decreasing null sequence, and let f be a decreasing function defined for all $x > a$, such that for some N, for all $n > N$,

$$f(n) = a_n.$$

(We shall often use the standard notation $\sum_{n=1}^{\infty} a_n$ for the series $a_1 + a_2 + \cdots + a_n + \cdots$.)

With the above setup the series $\sum_{n=1}^{\infty} a_n$ converges if the integral of f converges, and the series diverges if the integral of f diverges.

Proof

It is clear that

$$\int_{N+1}^{k} f < \sum_{n=N+1}^{k} a_n < \int_N^k f,$$

for every $k > N$, and the result follows.

This rather intuitively obvious fact has many applications, which we now sample.

Example A Consider the harmonic series

$$1 + \frac{1}{2} + \cdots + \frac{1}{n} + \cdots.$$

This series has decreasing terms which converge to 0. The corresponding function is

$$f(x) = \frac{1}{x}, \quad x \geq 1.$$

Now,

$$\int_1^n \frac{1}{x}\, dx = \log n.$$

Since $\lim_n \log n = +\infty$, the series diverges.

Example B Let $k > 1$, and consider the series

$$\frac{1}{1^k} + \frac{1}{2^k} + \cdots + \frac{1}{n^k} + \cdots.$$

This series has decreasing terms converging to 0. The corresponding function is

$$f(x) = \frac{1}{x^k}, \qquad x \geq 1.$$

now,

$$\int_1^n \frac{1}{x^k}\, dx = \frac{1}{1-k}(n^{1-k} - 1).$$

Since $\lim_n n^{1-k} = 0$, the series converges.

Example C The series $\sum_{n=2}^{\infty} 1/(n \log n)$ diverges, but $\sum_{n=1}^{\infty} 1/[n(\log n)^k]$ converges for every $k > 1$.

This follows because $\int dx/(x \log x) = (\log x)^2$ and $\int dx/[x(\log x)^k] = (\log x)^{1-k}/(1-k)$.

In similar fashion, it can be shown that for every m, the series

$$\sum_{n=N}^{\infty} \frac{1}{n \log n \cdots \log \cdots \log n}$$

diverges, but

$$\sum_{n=N}^{\infty} \frac{1}{n \log n \cdots (\log \cdots \log n)^k}$$

converges, for every $k > 1$, where N is chosen large enough for all denominators to be positive.

The above furnishes a scale of series which may be used for comparison tests. However, it is not hard to show that there are series to which this scale cannot be applied. Indeed, it can be shown that it is impossible to find any sequence of series which can be used as a comparison scale for all series. We shall give exercises at the end of this chapter illustrating this point.

3. SERIES WHOSE TERMS ARE POSITIVE AND NEGATIVE

We turn now to a discussion of series whose terms are neither all positive nor all negative.

Let

$$a_1 + a_2 + \cdots + a_n + \cdots$$

be such a series.

We base our discussion on two series

$$p_1 + p_2 + \cdots + p_n + \cdots$$

and

$$q_1 + q_2 + \cdots + q_n + \cdots,$$

obtained from the given series. The term p_1 is the first positive term of the given series, p_2 is the second positive term, etc. The series $\sum_{n=1}^{\infty} q_n$ has as its terms the negative terms of the series $\sum_{n=1}^{\infty} a_n$ in the same order in which they appear in this series.

Let $\{s_n\}$ be the sequence of partial sums of $\sum_{n=1}^{\infty} p_n$ and let $\{t_n\}$ be the sequence of partial sums of $\sum_{n=1}^{\infty} q_n$.

There are four possibilities.

Case 1. $\{s_n\}$ and $\{t_n\}$ are both bounded.
Case 2. $\{s_n\}$ is bounded and $\{t_n\}$ is unbounded.
Case 3. $\{s_n\}$ is unbounded and $\{t_n\}$ is bounded.
Case 4. $\{s_n\}$ and $\{t_n\}$ are both unbounded.

Two notions arise in this connection, absolute convergence and conditional convergence of series.

A series $a_1 + a_2 + \cdots + a_n + \cdots$ is said to be **absolutely convergent** if the associated series $|a_1| + |a_2| + \cdots + |a_n| + \cdots$ converges.

Theorem 3

A series which converges absolutely also converges.

Proof

Suppose $a_1 + a_2 + \cdots + a_n + \cdots$ converges absolutely. Let $\epsilon > 0$. There is an N such that $n > N$ and $p > 0$ implies $|a_{n+1}| + |a_{n+2}| + \cdots |a_{n+p}| < \epsilon$. But, $|a_{n+1} + \cdots + a_{n+p}| \leq |a_{n+1}| + \cdots + |a_{n+p}| < \epsilon$, so that $a_1 + a_2 + \cdots + a_n + \cdots$ converges. ∎

The converse is false. Consider the series $1 - 1/2 + 1/3 - 1/4 + \cdots$. We saw that it does not converge absolutely. However, it is easy to show that the series converges. Indeed, every series whose terms alternate in sign, are decreasing in absolute value, and converge to zero, is convergent. We leave the proof to the reader.

A series converges absolutely in Case 1 and only in Case 1.

Proof

Suppose Case 1 holds. There is an $M > 0$ such that $p_1 + \cdots + p_n < M$, for every n, and an $M' > 0$ such that $-(q_1 + \cdots + q_n) < M'$, for every n. Then, for every n, $|a_1| + \cdots + |a_n| < M + M'$, so that $a_1 + \cdots + a_n + \cdots$ converges absolutely.

That the series does not converge absolutely in Cases 2, 3, and 4 is apparent. Actually, in Case 2 the series diverges to $+\infty$ and in Case 3 the series diverges to $-\infty$. The proofs are easy and will be omitted.

In Case 4, anything can happen. As a matter of fact, the order in which the terms appear determines what happens in this case. We accordingly discuss rearrangement of series and see how it affects the four cases.

A **rearrangement** of the natural numbers is a bijective mapping

$$\phi\colon N \to N$$

and a **rearrangement** of a series

$$a_1 + a_2 + \cdots + a_n + \cdots$$

is the corresponding series

$$a_{\phi(1)} + a_{\phi(2)} + \cdots + a_{\phi(n)} + \cdots.$$

The notation

$$a_{k_1} + a_{k_2} + \cdots + a_{k_n} + \cdots$$

is standard and will be used.

For the first three cases, the order of terms does not matter. In Case 2, for example, for every rearrangement of the series, it is easy to show that the new series also diverges to $+\infty$, and a similar remark holds for Case 3.

Case 1 is more interesting. We have

Theorem 4

If a series $a_1 + a_2 + \cdots + a_n + \cdots$ converges absolutely, then every rearrangement converges absolutely and all rearrangements have the same sum.

Proof

Suppose $\sum_{n=1}^{\infty} |a_n| = M$. Then $\sum_{i=1}^{n} |a_{k_i}| \leq M$, for every rearrangement, and every n, so that every rearrangement converges absolutely.

Let $s = \sum_{n=1}^{\infty} a_n$, and let $\sum_{n=1}^{\infty} a_{k_n}$ be a rearrangement of $\sum_{n=1}^{\infty} a_n$. Let $\epsilon > 0$. There is an N such that $\left| s - \sum_{i=1}^{N} a_i \right| < \epsilon/2$, and $\sum_{i=N+1}^{\infty} |a_i| < \epsilon/2$. Let N' be such that $a_1, \ldots, a_N$ are among $a_{k_1}, \cdots, a_{k_{N'}}$. Then $n > N'$ implies

$$\left| s - \sum_{i=1}^{n} a_{k_i} \right| < \left| s - \sum_{i=1}^{N} a_i \right| + \sum_{i=N+1}^{\infty} |a_i| < \frac{\epsilon}{2} + \frac{\epsilon}{2} = \epsilon.$$

Thus, $s = \sum_{n=1}^{\infty} a_{k_n}$. ∎

In Case 4, we have convergence for some rearrangements and divergence for others. Suppose $\sum_{n=1}^{\infty} a_n$ is such that $\sum_{n=1}^{\infty} p_n = +\infty$ and $\sum_{n=1}^{\infty} q_n = -\infty$, but $\lim_n |a_n| = 0$. Let c be any real number. Let r_1 be the first natural number such that $p_1 + \cdots + p_{r_1} > c$. Let s_1 be the first natural number such that $p_1 + \cdots + p_{r_1} + q_1 + \cdots + q_{s_1} < c$. Then let r_2 be the first number, $r_2 > r_1$, such that $p_1 + \cdots + p_{r_1} + q_1 + \cdots q_{s_1} + p_{r_1+1} + \cdots + p_{r_2} > c$. Continuing in this way, we have a series which converges to c, which follows since $\lim_n |a_n| = 0$. This series is a rearrangement of $\sum_{n=1}^{\infty} a_n$.

A rearrangement which diverges to either $+\infty$ or $-\infty$ can also be managed. Thus, let $p_1 + \cdots + p_{r_1} > 1, p_1 + \cdots + p_{r_1} + q_1 + p_{r_1+1} + \cdots + p_{r_2} > 2$ and so on. A rearrangement is obtained which diverges to $+\infty$.

It is also possible to obtain rearrangements, in Case 4, for which the partial sums are bounded but do not converge. We do not wish to belabor this point, and leave it for the reader.

A series is called **conditionally convergent** if it converges but has a rearrangement which does not converge.

The proofs of the next two theorems are implicit in the above discussion.

Theorem 5

If a series converges conditionally, it has a rearrangement which has any prescribed sum.

Theorem 6

A convergent series converges conditionally if and only if it does not converge absolutely.

4. PRODUCT OF SERIES

Given two series $\sum_{n=1}^{\infty} a_n$ and $\sum_{n=1}^{\infty} b_n$, then their product should be a series whose terms are $a_n b_m$, $n, m = 1, 2, \cdots$. However, the order in which the terms should be taken is not clear. In one case, that of absolute convergence, the order does not matter and we discuss this case.

Let $\sum_{n=1}^{\infty} a_n$ and $\sum_{n=1}^{\infty} b_n$ be absolutely convergent. Then, a series whose terms are $a_n b_m$, $n, m = 1, 2, \cdots$ is also absolutely convergent. This is clear, since if

$$\sum_{n=1}^{\infty} |a_n| = M \quad \text{and} \quad \sum_{n=1}^{\infty} |b_n| = M',$$

then

$$\sum_{n,m=1}^{\infty} |a_n b_m| = MM'$$

where the order of addition does not matter. Moreover, the sum of the series $\sum_{n,m=1}^{\infty} a_n b_m$ is independent of order. We prove

Theorem 7

If $\sum_{n=1}^{\infty} a_n$ *and* $\sum_{n=1}^{\infty} b_n$ *converge absolutely, then*

$$\sum_{n,m=1}^{\infty} a_m b_n = \left(\sum_{n=1}^{\infty} a_n\right)\left(\sum_{n=1}^{\infty} b_n\right).$$

Proof

Let $\epsilon > 0$. Let $s = \sum_{n=1}^{\infty} a_n$, $t = \sum_{n=1}^{\infty} b_n$, and

$$\sum_{n=1}^{\infty} |a_n| + \sum_{n=1}^{\infty} |b_n| = M.$$

There is an N such that $n > N$ implies

$$\left| \sum_{i=1}^{n} a_i - s \right| < \frac{\epsilon}{4M},$$

$$\sum_{i=N+1}^{\infty} |a_i| < \frac{\epsilon}{4M},$$

$$\left| \sum_{i=1}^{n} b_i - t \right| < \frac{\epsilon}{4M},$$

$$\sum_{i=N+1}^{\infty} |b_i| < \frac{\epsilon}{4M}.$$

Let $\sum_{m,n=1}^{\infty} a_m b_n$ be given an arrangement and let N' be such that $a_i b_j$, $i, j = 1, \cdots, N$ are among the first N' terms of this series.

Let $r > N'$, and let $\Sigma' a_i b_j$ mean the sum of the first r terms of our arranged series. Then

$$|\Sigma' a_i b_j - st| < \left| \sum_{i,j=1}^{N} a_i b_j - st \right| + M \left(\sum_{i=N+1}^{\infty} |a_i| + \sum_{i=N+1}^{\infty} |b_i| \right).$$

But,

$$\begin{aligned} \left| \sum_{i,j=1}^{N} a_i b_j - st \right| &= \left| \sum_{i=1}^{N} a_i \sum_{i=1}^{N} b_i - st \right| \\ &\le \left| \sum_{i=1}^{N} a_i \sum_{i=1}^{N} b_i - s \sum_{i=1}^{N} b_i + s \sum_{i=1}^{N} b_i - st \right| \\ &\le M \left| \sum_{i=1}^{N} a_i - s \right| + M \left| \sum_{i=1}^{N} b_i - t \right| < \frac{\epsilon}{2}. \end{aligned}$$

It follows easily that

$$|\Sigma' a_i b_j - st| < \epsilon. \quad \blacksquare$$

It should be clear that this theorem can be proved by considering any special rearrangement of the product series. However, we feel that the present proof has merit.

EXERCISES

2.1 If $\sum_{n=1}^{\infty} a_n$ and $\sum_{n=1}^{\infty} b_n$ are convergent series of positive numbers, show that the series $\sum_{n=1}^{\infty} a_n^{1/2} b_n^{1/2}$ converges.

2.2 If $\sum_{n=1}^{\infty} a_n$ is a convergent series of positive numbers, and $p > 1$, show that $\sum_{n=1}^{\infty} a_n^p$ converges.

2.3 Give an example of a convergent series $\sum_{n=1}^{\infty} a_n$ of positive terms, such that the series $\sum_{n=1}^{\infty} a_n^p$ diverges for every p, with $0 < p < 1$.

2.4 Given a sequence of series of positive terms, each of which converges, show that there is a series which converges more slowly than all of them.

2.5 Given an example of a series of positive terms which converges more slowly than all the series

$$\frac{1}{n \log n \log\log n \cdots \underbrace{(\log \cdots \log n)^2}_{m}},$$

$m = 1, 2, \cdots$.

2.6 Show that if $\sum_{n=1}^{\infty} a_n$ is a convergent series of positive terms which are decreasing, then $\lim_n na_n = 0$.

2.7 Show that the converse of Exercise 2.6 does not hold.

2.8 If $\sum_{n=1}^{\infty} a_n$ is a series of decreasing positive terms, and $\sum_{n=1}^{\infty} (a_n a_{n+1})^{1/2}$ converges, show that $\sum_{n=1}^{\infty} a_n$ converges.

2.9 An infinite product $\prod_{n=1}^{\infty} (1 + a_n)$, $a_n > 0$, $n = 1, 2, \cdots$, is said to be convergent if the sequence $s_n = \prod_{k=1}^{n} (1 + a_k)$ converges. Show that the infinite product converges if and only if the infinite series $\sum_{n=1}^{\infty} a_n$ converges.

2.10 For what values of p does the series

$$1 + \left(\frac{1}{2}\right)^p + \left(\frac{1 \cdot 3}{2 \cdot 4}\right)^p + \cdots$$

converge?

2.11 Generalize the result of Exercise 2.10.

2.12 If $\sum_{n=1}^{\infty} a_n$ is an infinite series of positive terms, show that it converges if

$$\liminf_n \left[n\left(\frac{a_n}{a_{n+1}} - 1\right)\right] > 1.$$

2.13 Show that it diverges if

$$\limsup_n \left[n\left(\frac{a_n}{a_{n+1}} - 1\right)\right] < 1.$$

2.14 Give an example which cannot be treated by the results of Exercises 2.12 and 2.13.

2.15 Does the series

$$\frac{1}{\log 2} + \frac{1}{\log 3} + \cdots + \frac{1}{\log n} + \cdots$$

converge or diverge?

2.16 Does the series $\sum_{n=1}^{\infty} \frac{e^n n!}{n^n}$ converge or diverge?

2.17 If $\sum_{n=1}^{\infty} a_n^2 < \infty$ and $\sum_{n=1}^{\infty} b_n^2 < \infty$, show that

$$\left(\sum_{n=1}^{\infty} a_n b_n\right)^2 \leq \sum_{n=1}^{\infty} a_n^2 \sum_{n=1}^{\infty} b_n^2.$$

2.18 If $\sum_{n=1}^{\infty} a_n^2 < \infty$ and $\sum_{n=1}^{\infty} b_n^2 < \infty$ show that

$$\left[\sum_{n=1}^{\infty} (a_n + b_n)^2\right]^{1/2} \leq \left[\sum_{n=1}^{\infty} a_n^2\right]^{1/2} + \left[\sum_{=1n}^{\infty} b_n^2\right]^{1/2}.$$

3.1 If $a_1, \cdots, a_n$ and $b_1, \cdots, b_n$ are given, with $s_k = a_1 + \cdots + a_k$, $k = 1, \cdots, n$, show that

$$\sum_{k=1}^{\infty} a_k b_k = \sum_{n=1}^{\infty} s_{k-1}(b_{k-1} - b_k) + s_n b_n.$$

3.2 If the sequence $\{s_n\}$ of partial sums of $\sum_{n=1}^{\infty} a_n$ is bounded and the sequence $\{b_n\}$ is nonincreasing and converges to zero, then the series $\sum_{n=1}^{\infty} a_n b_n$ converges.

3.3 If $\sum_{n=1}^{\infty} a_n$ converges and $\{b_n\}$ is nonincreasing, show that $\sum_{n=1}^{\infty} a_n b_n$ converges.

3.4 If the terms of a series alternate in sign, decrease in absolute value, and converge to zero, show that the series converges.

3.5 Given any closed interval $[a, b]$, show that every conditionally convergent series has a rearrangement which has $[a, b]$ as the set of limit points of its sequence of partial sums.

3.6 Give an example of a series for which $\sum_{n=1}^{\infty} a_n$ converges but $\sum_{n=1}^{\infty} a_n^2$ diverges.

3.7 If every subseries of a series converges, show that the series converges absolutely.

4.1 If $\sum_{n=0}^{\infty} a_n$ and $\sum_{n=0}^{\infty} b_n$ are series, its Cauchy product is defined as the series $\sum_{n=0}^{\infty} c_n$, where

$$c_n = a_0 b_n + a_1 b_{n-1} + \cdots + a_n b_0.$$

Give an example of two divergent series whose Cauchy product converges.

4.2 If $\sum_{n=1}^{\infty} a_n$ converges to A, $\sum_{n=0}^{\infty} b_n$ converges to B, and $\sum_{n=0}^{\infty} a_n$ converges absolutely, show that their Cauchy product converges to AB.

4.3 If $\sum_{n=1}^{\infty} a_n = s$, $\sum_{n=0}^{\infty} b_n = t$, and their Cauchy product $\sum_{n=1}^{\infty} c_n$ converges, show that $\sum_{n=0}^{\infty} c_n = st$.

CHAPTER 4

CONTINUOUS FUNCTIONS

1. FUNCTIONS DEFINED ON R

We first consider **functions** whose domain is the whole real line. By this we mean a mapping

$$f\colon \mathrm{R} \to \mathrm{R}.$$

A function f is said to be **continuous** at $x \in \mathrm{R}$ if, for every sequence $\{x_n\}$ which converges to x, we have

$$\lim_n f(x_n) = f(x).$$

Then, f is said to be **continuous** if it is continuous at every $x \in \mathrm{R}$.

Theorem 1

A function f is continuous at x if and only if, for every $\epsilon > 0$, there is a $\delta > 0$ such that $|x - y| < \delta$ implies $|f(x) - f(y)| < \epsilon$.

Proof

Suppose that, for every $\epsilon > 0$, there is a $\delta > 0$ such that $|x - y| < \delta$ implies $|f(x) - f(y)| < \epsilon$. Let $\{x_n\}$ be such that $\lim_n x_n = x$. Let $\epsilon > 0$. There is a $\delta > 0$ such that $|x - y| < \delta$ implies $|f(x) - f(y)| < \epsilon$. There is an N such that $n > N$ implies $|x - x_n| < \delta$. Then $n > N$ implies $|f(x) - f(x_n)| < \epsilon$, so that f is continuous at x.

Suppose there is a $k > 0$ such that, for every $\delta > 0$ there is a y such that $|y - x| < \delta$ and $|f(x) - f(y)| \geq k$. Then, for every n, there is an x_n such that $|x - x_n| < 1/n$ and $|f(x) - f(x_n)| \geq k$. Then $\lim_n x_n = x$, but $\lim_n f(x_n) \neq f(x)$. Thus f is not continuous at x. ∎

Example A The function f given by $f(x) = x^k$ is continuous for every natural number k.

We have already shown that $\lim_n s_n = s$ implies $\lim_n s_n^k = s^k$. The result thus follows by the definition of continuity.

Example B The function f given by $f(x) = x^{1/k}$ is continuous at every $x > 0$, where k is any natural number.

We use the fact that

$$x - y = (x^{1/k} - y^{1/k})(x^{(k-1)/k} + x^{(k-2)/k}y^{1/k} + \cdots + y^{(k-1)/k}).$$

If $y > x/2$, then

$$x^{(k-1)/k} + x^{(k-2)/k}y^{1/k} + \cdots + y^{(k-1)/k} > \frac{k}{2}x^{(k-1)/k}.$$

Let $\epsilon > 0$. For $\delta = \min\left[\frac{x}{2}, \frac{k}{2}x^{(k-1)/k}\epsilon\right]$, $|x - y| < \delta$ implies

$$|x^{1/k} - y^{1/k}| < \delta \cdot \frac{2}{k}x^{k/(k-1)} < \epsilon.$$

If S is any set, the **inverse image,** $f^{-1}(S)$, of S under f is the set

$$f^{-1}(S) = [x: f(x) \in S].$$

Theorem 2

A function f: R → R is continuous if and only if, for every open set G, the inverse image, $f^{-1}(G)$, is open.

Proof

Suppose f is continuous, and G is an open set. Let $x \in f^{-1}(G)$. Then $f(x) \in G$ and, since G is open there is an $\epsilon > 0$ such that $J = (f(x) - \epsilon, f(x) + \epsilon) \subset G$. There is a $\delta > 0$ such that $|x - y| < \delta$ implies $f(x) \in J$. Thus $(x - \delta, x + \delta) \subset f^{-1}(G)$.

Suppose there is an x at which f is not continuous. Then there is an $\epsilon > 0$ such that, for every $\delta > 0$, there is a y such that $|y - x| < \delta$ and $f(y) \notin J = (f(x) - \epsilon, f(x) + \epsilon)$. Then J is an open set, but $f^{-1}(J)$ is not open since $x \in f^{-1}(J)$ but every open interval containing x contains points not in $f^{-1}(J)$. ∎

2. SETS OF POINTS OF DISCONTINUITY

Let f: R $\to$ R be a function, and let I be an open interval. If the set $[f(x): x \in I]$ has an upper bound, we let

$$u(f, I)$$

be the least upper bound, and write

$$u(f, I) = \sup [f(x): x \in I].$$

Otherwise, we let

$$u(f, I) = +\infty.$$

Similarly, if the set $[f(x): x \in I]$ has a lower bound, we let

$$l(f, I)$$

be its greatest lower bound, and write

$$l(f, I) = \inf [f(x): x \in I].$$

Otherwise, we let

$$l(f, I) = -\infty.$$

We define the **saltus** of f in I as

$$w(f, I) = u(f, I) - l(f, I).$$

Then $w(f, I) \geq 0$, and $w(f, I) = +\infty$ if and only if either $u(f, I) = +\infty$ or $l(f, I) = -\infty$.

We now define the **saltus,** $w(f, x)$, of f at a point x as the greatest lower bound of the set of numbers $w(f, I)$ as I varies over open intervals with $x \in I$.

Theorem 3

The function f is continuous at x if and only if $w(f, x) = 0$.

Proof

Suppose $w(f, x) = 0$. Let $\epsilon > 0$. There is an open interval J such that $x \in J$ and $w(f, J) < \epsilon$. Then $y \in J$ implies $|f(x) - f(y)| < \epsilon$, so that f is continuous at x.

Suppose f is continuous at x. Let $\epsilon > 0$. There is a $\delta > 0$ such that $|x - y| < \delta$ implies $|f(x) - f(y)| < \epsilon/2$. Let $J = (x - \delta, x + \delta)$. Then $w(f, J) < \epsilon$. It follows that $w(f, x) = 0$. ∎

We use the above to classify the sets of points of discontinuity of an arbitrary function. Let $k > 0$. Suppose $w(f, x) < k$. Then there is an open interval J such that $x \in J$ and $w(f, J) < k$. It follows that for every $y \in J$, $w(f, y) < k$. Hence, the set of points for which $w(f, x) < k$ is an open set. The set D_k of points for which $w(f, x) \geq k$ is then closed. If D is the set of points of discontinuity of f, then

$$D = \bigcup_{n=1}^{\infty} D_{1/n}.$$

We thus have

Theorem 4

If $f\colon \mathrm{R} \to \mathrm{R}$ is any function, the set D of points of discontinuity of f is the union of a countable number of closed sets.

Example A Let $\{r_n\}$ be the set of rational numbers written as a sequence. Let f be defined by

$$f(x) = \begin{cases} \dfrac{1}{n} & x = r_n \\ 0 & x \text{ irrational.} \end{cases}$$

We show that f is discontinuous at every rational and continuous at every irrational. Since every interval contains irrationals, $w(f, r_n) \geq 1/n$. Let x be irrational and let $\epsilon > 0$. There is an N such that $1/N < \epsilon$. Let J be an open interval which contains x but none of the rationals $r_1, r_2, \ldots, r_N$. Then $w(f, J) < \epsilon$, so that f is continuous at x.

Example B We show that there is no function which is continuous at every rational and discontinuous at every irrational. In other words, we show that the set of irrationals is not the union of a countable number of closed sets. This will be accomplished when we show that if $S = \bigcup_{n=1}^{\infty} S_n$, where each S_n is closed, and if S contains no interval, then $\mathscr{C}S$ is uncountable.

Let $T \subset \mathscr{C}S$ be countable, with elements $a_1, a_2, \cdots, a_n, \cdots$. We show that there is an $a \in \mathscr{C}S$, $a \notin T$. First, $\mathscr{C}S_1$ contains a closed interval I_1 such that $a_1 \notin I_1$. Then $\mathscr{C}S_2$ contains a closed interval $I_2 \subset I_1$ such that $a_2 \notin I_2$. In this way, we obtain closed intervals

$$I_1 \supset I_2 \supset \cdots \supset I_n \supset \cdots$$

such that, for every n, $a_n \notin I_n$, and $S_n \cap I_n$ is empty. Let $a \in \bigcap_{n=1}^{\infty} I_n$. Then $a \notin S$ and $a \neq a_n$, $n = 1, 2, \cdots$. This proves that $\mathscr{C}S$ is uncountable.

3. SOME SIMPLE FACTS

We prove some simple things which will be used later.

(a) If $f\colon R \to R$ is continuous and is zero on a dense set (i.e., a set whose intersection with every interval is nonempty), then f is identically zero.

Proof

Let $x \in R$. There is a sequence $\{x_n\}$ such that $\lim_n x_n = x$, and $f(x_n) = 0$, $n = 1, 2, \cdots$. Then $f(x) = 0$. ∎

(b) If $f\colon R \to R$ is continuous, $f(x) > 0$, for every x, and I is a closed interval, there is a $k > 0$ such that $f(x) > k$, for every $x \in I$.

Proof

Let $x \in I$. Since f is continuous at x and $f(x) > 0$, there is an open interval J_x and a $k_x > 0$ such that $f(y) > k_x$ for every $y \in J_x$. Let $\mathscr{J} = [J_x\colon x \in I]$. By the Borel covering theorem, a finite subset $[J_{x_1}, \cdots, J_{x_n}]$ of $\mathscr{J}$ covers I. Let $k = \min\,[k_{x_1}, \cdots, k_{x_n}]$. Then $k > 0$ and $f(x) > k$ for every $x \in I$. ∎

A real function f is called **monotonically nondecreasing** if $x > y$ implies $f(x) \geq f(y)$.

(c) If $f\colon R \to R$ is monotonically nondecreasing, its set of points of discontinuity is countable.

Proof

We show that for every a, b, with $a < b$, and every natural number n, the set of points at which

$$w(f, x) > \frac{1}{n}[f(b) - f(a)]$$

is finite. In fact there are fewer than n such points.

Suppose, on the contrary, that

$$a < x_1 < x_2 < \cdots < x_n < b$$

and $w(f, x_i) > \dfrac{1}{n}(f(b) - f(a)]$, $\qquad i = 1, \cdots, n.$

It follows that there are

$$a < y_1 < x_1 < z_1 < y_2 < x_2 < \cdots < y_n < x_n < z_n < b$$

such that

$$f(z_i) - f(y_i) > \frac{1}{n}[f(b) - f(a)], \qquad i = 1, \cdots, n.$$

But, then,

$$f(b) - f(a) \geqq \sum_{i=1}^{n} [f(z_i) - f(y_i)]$$
$$> \sum_{i=1}^{n} \frac{1}{n} [f(b) - f(a)] = f(b) - f(a).$$

This is clearly impossible.

Now, if D_n is the set of points on (a, b) at which

$$w(f, x) > \frac{1}{n} [f(b) - f(a)],$$

and D is the set of points of discontinuity of f on (a, b), then $D = \bigcup_{n=1}^{\infty} D_n$. It follows that D, as the union of a countable number of finite sets, is countable. If a set S has countable intersection with every interval, it is easy to show that S is countable, so that our result follows. ∎

4. THE CLASS OF CONTINUOUS FUNCTIONS

The purpose of this section is to show that continuity is preserved by the standard algebraic operations on functions.

(a) If f and g are continuous, then $f + g$ is continuous.

Proof

Suppose f and g are both continuous at a point x. Then $\lim_n x_n = x$ implies $\lim_n f(x_n) = f(x)$ and $\lim_n g(x_n) = g(x)$. It follows that

$$\lim_n (f(x_n) + g(x_n)) = f(x) + g(x).$$

Hence, $f + g$ is continuous at x. ∎

(b) If f and g are continuous, then fg is continuous.

Proof

Suppose f and g are both continuous at a point x. Then $\lim_n x_n = x$ implies $\lim_n f(x_n) = f(x)$ and $\lim_n g(x_n) = g(x)$. It follows that

$$\lim_n f(x_n)g(x_n) = f(x)g(x),$$

so that fg is continuous at x. ∎

(c) If f is continuous and $a \in \mathrm{R}$, then af is continuous.

Proof

Suppose f is continuous at x. Then $\lim_n x_n = x$ implies $\lim_n f(x_n) = f(x)$. It follows that $\lim_n af(x_n) = af(x)$, so that af is continuous at x. ∎

(d) If f and g are continuous at x, and $g(x) \neq 0$, then $\frac{f}{g}$ is continuous at x.

Proof

Now, $\lim_n x_n = x$ implies $\lim_n f(x_n) = f(x)$ and $\lim_n g(x_n) = g(x) \neq 0$. Then, there is an N such that $n > N$ implies $g(x_n) \neq 0$. It follows that $\lim_n \frac{f(x_n)}{g(x_n)} = \frac{f(x)}{g(x)}$. ∎

(e) If f is continuous, then $|f|$ is continuous.

Proof

It is easy to show that if $a, b \in R$, then $||a| - |b|| \leq |a - b|$. Then, for every x, y,

$$||f(x)| - |f(y)|| \leq |f(x) - f(y)|.$$

Since f is continuous at $x \in \mathrm{R}$, for every $\epsilon > 0$, there is a $\delta > 0$ such that $|x - y| < \delta$ implies $|f(x) - f(y)| < \epsilon$, so that $||f(x)| - |f(y)|| < \epsilon$. Thus $|f|$ is continuous at x.

(f) If f and g are continuous, then $\max(f, g)$ and $\min(f, g)$ are continuous.

Remark The function $\max(f, g)$ is defined by

$$[\max(f, g)](x) = \max(f(x), g(x))$$

for every x.

Proof

We note that

$$\max(f, g) = \tfrac{1}{2}(f + g) + \tfrac{1}{2}|f - g|$$

and

$$\min(f, g) = \tfrac{1}{2}(f + g) - \tfrac{1}{2}|f - g|.$$

The result follows from (a), (c), and (d). ∎

5. PROPERTIES OF CONTINUOUS FUNCTIONS

We now prove some deeper properties of continuous functions.

(a) If f: R → R is continuous, then f is bounded on every closed interval I.

Proof

Suppose I is a closed interval, and f is unbounded on I. Then for every n, there is an $x_n \in I$ such that $|f(x_n)| > n$. The sequence $\{x_n\}$ has a convergent subsequence $\{x_{n_k}\}$ with

$$\lim_k x_{n_k} = x \in I.$$

Since the sequence $\{f(x_{n_k})\}$ is unbounded, it cannot converge to $f(x)$. Thus f cannot be continuous at x. This contradicts the assumption that f is unbounded on I. ∎

(b) If f: R → R is continuous, then f has a maximum on every closed interval I, i.e., there is an $x \in I$ such that $f(x) \geq f(y)$, for every $y \in I$.

Proof

By **(a)**, f is bounded on I. Let

$$u = \sup [f(x) : x \in I].$$

For every n, there is then an $x_n \in I$ such that $f(x_n) > u - 1/n$. Then $\lim_n f(x_n) = u$. Now, $\{x_n\}$ has a convergent subsequence $\{x_{n_k}\}$ such that $\lim_k x_{n_k} = x \in I$. Then $\lim_k f(x_{n_k}) = u$. Since f is continuous, $\lim_k f(x_{n_k}) = f(x)$. Hence, $u = f(x)$. ∎

(c) If f: R → R is continuous, then f has a minimum on every closed interval I.

The proof is the same as for (*b*).

(d) If f: R → R is continuous, if $a < b$, and if c is any number between $f(a)$ and $f(b)$, there is an x between a and b such that $f(x) = c$.

Proof

It suffices to prove that if $f(a) < 0 < f(b)$ there is an $x \in (a, b)$ such that $f(x) = 0$. Let

$$E = [x : x \in [a, b], f(x) < 0],$$

and let $u = \sup E$. Then $a < u < b$. There are sequences $\{x_n\}$ in E and $\{y_n\}$ in $\mathscr{C}E$, both converging to u. Since f is continuous, $f(u) = \lim_n f(x_n) \leq 0$ and $f(u) = \lim_n f(y_n) \geq 0$. Thus, $f(u) = 0$. ∎

We are now ready to show that the inverse of every strictly increasing continuous function is continuous. We proceed to define these notions.

A function f: R → R is *strictly increasing* if $x > y$ implies $f(x) > f(y)$.

Suppose f: R → R is injective, and let $S = f(\mathrm{R})$. The **inverse** function

$$f^{-1}: S \to \mathrm{R}$$

is defined by $f^{-1}(y) = x$, where $f(x) = y$, for every $y \in S$.

If f: R → R is continuous and strictly increasing, then $f(\mathrm{R}) = J$, where J is an open interval. This follows from **(d)**, since if $a < b$, then for every $c \in [f(a), f(b)]$, there is an $x \in (a, b)$ such that $f(x) = c$; for every $a' < a, f(a') < f(a)$; for every $b' > b, f(b') > f(b)$.

Theorem 8

If f: R → R is strictly increasing and continuous, and if $J = f(\mathrm{R})$, then

$$f^{-1}: J \to \mathrm{R}$$

is strictly increasing and continuous.

Proof

Only the continuity of f^{-1} requires proof. Let $y \in J$. There is an x such that $y = f(x)$.

Let $\epsilon > 0$. There is a $\delta > 0$, $\delta < \epsilon$, such that

$$f(x) - f(x - \delta) < \epsilon \quad \text{and} \quad f(x + \delta) - f(x) < \epsilon$$

Let $f(x - \delta) = y_1$ and $f(x + \delta) = y_2$. Then $y_1 < y < y_2$. Let $\delta' = \min(y - y_1, y_2 - y)$. Then $\delta' > 0$, and $|y - y'| < \delta'$ implies $|f^{-1}(y) - f^{-1}(y')| < \delta < \epsilon$, so that f^{-1} is continuous at y. ∎

6. FUNCTIONS DEFINED ON ARBITRARY SETS

In the last section, we found it necessary to consider a function f^{-1} which may be defined on a proper subset of the reals.

We now consider functions, which are defined on subsets of the reals, in some detail. Let

$$f: A \to \mathrm{R}$$

where $A \subset \mathrm{R}$. The set A is called the **domain** of f.

The function f is said to be **continuous** at $x \in A$ if, whenever $\lim_n x_n = x$, $x_n \in A$, $n = 1, 2, \cdots$, it follows that $\lim_n f(x_n) = f(x)$.

Sometimes the following complication arises. We have a function

$$f: A \to \mathrm{R}$$

and a set $B \subset A$. We wish to consider the restriction of f to B. This may be regarded as a new function

$$F: B \to R$$

where, for every $x \in B$, $F(x) = f(x)$. Then F is called the **restriction** of f to the set B. Also, f is called the **extension** of F to the set A.

It is possible for F to be continuous at $x \in B$ while f is not continuous at x. For example, let $f: \mathrm{R} \to \mathrm{R}$ be defined by

$$f(x) = \begin{cases} 1 & x \text{ rational} \\ 0 & x \text{ irrational.} \end{cases}$$

Let F be the restriction of f to the set S of irrational numbers. Then F is continuous at every point in its domain S, but f is not continuous anywhere. In such a situation, it may be said that f is continuous on the irrationals relative to the irrationals.

More generally, if $f: A \to \mathrm{R}$, $B \subset A$, and the restriction F of f to B is continuous, we may say that f is **continuous on B, relative to B.**

Let S be any subset of R. We may regard S as the whole space, not merely as a subset of R, and define open and closed sets in S.

A set $G \subset S$ is said to be **open (relative to S)** if, for every $x \in G$ there is a $\delta > 0$ such that $y \in S$ and $|x - y| < \delta$ implies $y \in G$. A set $F \subset S$ is said to be **closed (relative to S)** if its complement in S, i.e., the set of $x \in S$, $x \notin F$, is open (relative to S).

It follows that $F \subset S$ is closed (relative to S) if and only if every limit point of F, which is in S, belongs to F. Moreover, it is easy to see that $G \subset S$ is open (relative to S) if and only if there is an H, open in R, such that $G = H \cap S$, and $F \subset S$ is closed (relative to S) if and only if there is a K, closed in R, such that $F = K \cap S$.

We now state

Theorem 2′

If $f: S \to \mathrm{R}$, then f is continuous if and only if for every open $G \subset \mathrm{R}$, $f^{-1}(G)$ is open relative to S.

The proof, which differs only in detail from that of Theorem 2, is left to the reader.

We shall consider functions whose domains are closed bounded sets, or **compact** sets. In the next few statements we assume S compact.

(a) If $S \subset \mathrm{R}$ is compact and

$$f\colon S \to \mathrm{R}$$

is continuous, then f is bounded.

(b) If $S \subset \mathrm{R}$ is compact and

$$f\colon S \to \mathrm{R}$$

is continuous, then f has a maximum on S and f has a minimum on S.

The proofs of **(a)** and **(b)** differ little from the proofs for the case where S is a closed interval. The proofs are accordingly left to the reader.

7. UNIFORM CONTINUITY

Continuity is a local concept. In other words, a function has been defined to be continuous if it is continuous at every point. A related global concept, which is of great importance, is that of uniform continuity.

A function

$$f\colon S \to \mathrm{R}$$

is said to be **uniformly continuous** if, for every $\varepsilon > 0$ there is a $\delta > 0$ such that for every $x \in S$ and $y \in S$, $|x - y| < \delta$ implies $|f(x) - f(y)| < \epsilon$.

It is clear that if $f\colon S \to \mathrm{R}$ is uniformly continuous, then it is continuous. However, the converse is false. We give two examples.

Example A Let $f\colon \mathrm{R} \to \mathrm{R}$ be defined by $f(x) = x^2$, $x \in \mathrm{R}$.

We have already observed that f is continuous. However, f is not uniformly continuous. For this purpose, let $h > 0$, $x = 1/h$, $y = 1/h + h$. Then

$$f(y) - f(x) = \left(\frac{1}{h} + h\right)^2 - \left(\frac{1}{h}\right)^2 > 2.$$

Example B Let R^+ be the set of positive reals, and let $f\colon \mathrm{R}^+ \to \mathrm{R}$ be defined by $f(x) = \sin 1/x$. The continuity follows from the continuity of the composition of continuous functions, the continuity of $1/x$ and of $\sin x$. For the latter, we note that $|\sin x - \sin y| < |x - y|$ for x, y. (We shall discuss the sine function in detail later.)

That the function is not uniformly continuous follows since, for every δ, there is an n such that $2/(n\pi) - 2/[(n+1)\pi] < \delta$, but $|\sin (n\pi)/2 - \sin [(n+1)\pi]/2| = 1$.

However, we prove the important

Theorem 9

If S is compact and

$$f: S \to \mathrm{R}$$

is continuous, then it is uniformly continuous.

Proof

If f is not uniformly continuous, there is an $r > 0$ such that for every n, there are $x_n \in S$, $y_n \in S$ such that $|x_n - y_n| < 1/n$ but $|f(x_n) - f(y_n)| > r$. Now, since S is compact, $\{x_n\}$ has a subsequence $\{x_{n_k}\}$ which converges to $x \in S$. But, it is clear that $\{y_{n_k}\}$ also converges to x. However, it is not true that $\lim_k f(x_{n_k}) = \lim_k f(y_{n_k})$ since $|f(x_{n_k}) - f(y_{n_k})| > r$ for every k. This contradicts the assumed continuity of f at x. ∎

We close this section by showing that every continuous function on a closed interval may be approximated by especially simple functions.

Let $I = [a, b]$ be a closed interval. A function

$$f: I \to \mathrm{R}$$

will be called a **step** function if there is a partition $a = x_0 < x_1 < \cdots < x_n = b$ and there are constants $c_1, \cdots, c_n$ such that

$$f(x) = \begin{cases} c_i, & x_{i-1} \le x < x_i, \quad i = 1, \cdots, n-1 \\ c_n & x_{n-1} \le x \le x_n. \end{cases}$$

A function

$$f: I \to \mathrm{R}$$

will be called **quasilinear** if there is a partition $a = x_0 < x_1 < \cdots < x_n = b$ such that f is linear on each interval $[x_{i-1}, x_i]$, $i = 1, \cdots, n$, and f is continuous on I.

It is easy to show that:

If $f: I \to \mathrm{R}$ is continuous, where $I = [a, b]$ is a closed interval, then for every $\epsilon > 0$, there are a step function g and a quasilinear function h such that

$$|f(x) - g(x)| < \epsilon \quad \text{and} \quad |f(x) - h(x)| < \epsilon$$

for every $x \in I$.

Proof

f is uniformly continuous on I. It follows that there is a partition $a = x_0 < x_1 < \cdots < x_n = b$ such that the saltus of f is less than ϵ on each interval $[x_{i-1}, x_i]$, $i = 1, \cdots, n$. The construction of the functions g and h becomes evident. ▮

EXERCISES

1.1 Give a proof that $f(x) = x^k$, k a natural number, is continuous at $x = x_0$ by exhibiting a $\delta > 0$, for every $\epsilon > 0$, such that $|x - x_0| < \delta$ implies $|f(x) - f(x_0)| < \epsilon$.

1.2 Do the same as in Exercise 1.1 for the function $f(x) = 1/\sqrt{x_0}$, $x_0 > 0$.

1.3 A point x_0 is said to be a relative minimum of a function f if there is an open interval J such that $x_0 \in J$ and $x \in J$ implies $f(x) \geq f(x_0)$. Show that if every x is a relative minimum of f, and f is continuous, then f is constant.

1.4 Show that if f is unrestricted except that every x is a relative minimum of f, then the value set of f is countable.

2.1 Given any closed set S, construct a function whose set of points of discontinuity is precisely S.

2.2 Given any set S, which is the union of countably many closed sets, construct a function whose set of points of discontinuity is precisely S.

2.3 Let g be defined for $x > 0$ in such a way as to be positive, increasing, with $\lim_{x \to 0} g(x) = 0$. Then g is said to be the modulus of continuity of a function f if for every $x \neq y$,

$$|f(x) - f(y)| < g(|x - y|).$$

Show that every continuous function, on a closed interval, has a modulus of continuity.

2.4 Is the same true for continuous functions on the reals?

2.5 Given any g as in Exercise 2.3, show that there is a continuous function on $[0, 1]$ for which it is not the modulus of continuity.

3.1 A function f is said to be right continuous at a point x_0 if, for every $\epsilon > 0$, there is a $\delta > 0$ such that $x_0 < x < x_0 + \delta$ implies $|f(x) - f(x_0)| < \epsilon$. Show that every monotonically nondecreasing function f can be changed on a countable set so as to become right continuous everywhere.

3.2 The right limit of f is said to exist at x_0 if there is a k such that, for every $\epsilon > 0$, there is a $\delta > 0$ such that $x_0 < x < x_0 + \delta$ implies $|f(x) - k| < \epsilon$. A similar definition applies to the left limit. Show that if f is such that its right and left limits exist everywhere, then its set of points of discontinuity is countable.

3.3 If D is any countable set, show that there is a function f whose right and left limits exist everywhere for which D is the set of points of discontinuity.

4.1 Show that if f and g are continuous then $g \circ f$ is continuous.

4.2 A function f is said to be lower semicontinuous at x_0 if $\lim\limits_n x_n = x_0$ implies $\liminf\limits_n f(x_n) \geq f(x_0)$. Show that f is lower semicontinuous at x_0 if and only if, for every $\epsilon > 0$, there is a $\delta > 0$ such that $|x - x_0| < \delta$ implies $f(x) > f(x_0) - \epsilon$.

4.3 Show that f is lower semicontinuous everywhere if and only if for every k, the set of points for which $f(x) \leq k$ is closed.

4.4 If f is lower semicontinuous on a closed interval $[a, b]$, then f is bounded from below on $[a, b]$.

4.5 If f is lower semicontinuous on a closed interval $[a, b]$, show that f attains its minimum on $[a, b]$.

4.6 Define upper semicontinuity and prove statements analogous to those of Exercises 4.2, 4.3, 4.4, and 4.5.

4.7 Show that for any f the saltus function of f is upper semicontinuous.

4.8 Show that the sum and product of two lower semicontinuous functions is lower semicontinuous.

4.9 Show that if every point is a relative minimum of f then f is lower semicontinuous. Moreover, in this case, the set of points of continuity of f contains a dense open set.

7.1 Show that an unbounded function on a finite open interval cannot be uniformly continuous.

7.2 Prove, using the Borel covering theorem, that a continuous function on a closed interval is uniformly continuous.

7.3 If S is compact and f is continuous on S show that it is uniformly continuous.

7.4 Characterize the sets S such that every function continuous on S is uniformly continuous.

7.5 If f is continuous on a closed interval $[a, b]$, show that for every $\epsilon > 0$ there is a quasilinear g such that $|f(x) - g(x)| < \epsilon$ for every $x \in [a, b]$.

CHAPTER 5

SPECIAL FUNCTIONS

1. LINEAR FUNCTIONS

We have shown in Chapter 4 that if f is continuous, and is zero on a dense set, then f is identically zero. It follows that if f and g are continuous, and if $f(x) = g(x)$ for every x in a dense set, then f is identical with g. We shall use this elementary, but important, fact several times in this chapter.

We first consider linear functions. A real function

$$f\colon \mathrm{R} \rightarrow \mathrm{R}$$

is said to be **linear** if, for every $x, y \in \mathrm{R}$

$$f(x + y) = f(x) + f(y).$$

In particular, for every $c \in \mathrm{R}$, the function f, for which

$$f(x) = cx$$

for every $x \in \mathrm{R}$, is linear. Indeed, $f(x + y) = c \cdot (x + y) = cx + cy = f(x) + f(y)$. These functions are also continuous.

The interesting fact is that every continuous linear function is of this type.

In order to prove this, let f be linear and suppose

$$f(1) = c.$$

It then follows from the linearity of f that, for every rational r,

$$f(r) = cr.$$

We suppose further that f is continuous. Since f agrees on the rationals with the function whose value is cx, for every x, it follows that f is this function.

There are discontinuous linear functions which are not of this type. They are quite pathological and we do not discuss them here.

2. THE FUNCTIONS a^x

We know the meaning of a^r for rationals r, and $a > 0$. Indeed, this definition is made so that the law of exponents

$$a^{r+s} = a^r \cdot a^s$$

should hold. In particular, for n a natural number,

$$a^0 = 1, \quad a^{-n} = \frac{1}{a^n}, \quad \text{and} \quad a^{1/n} = \sqrt[n]{a}.$$

Suppose $a > 1$. Then if r and s are rationals, with $r < s$, it follows that $a^r < a^s$. For every real number x, we define a^x by

$$a^x = \sup\,[a^r: r \text{ rational}, r < x].$$

It follows that the function a^x is defined for all real x and is strictly increasing since, if $x < y$, there is a rational r such that $x < r < y$.

We shall prove that a^x is continuous. We first prove the continuity at $x = 0$.

Let $\epsilon > 0$. There is an $n > a$ such that $1 < \sqrt[n]{n} < 1 + \epsilon$. Let $r < 1/n$ be positive. Then

$$a^r < n^{1/n} < 1 + \epsilon,$$

so that $x_n > 0$, $n = 1, 2, \cdots$, and $\lim_n x_n = 0$, implies $\lim_n a^{x_n} = 1$. Moreover, $\lim_n a^{-x_n} = \lim_n \dfrac{1}{a^{x_n}} = 1$. Hence, a^x is continuous at $x = 0$.

We next show that, for every $x, y \in \mathrm{R}$,

$$a^{x+y} = a^x \cdot a^y.$$

Let $\epsilon > 0$ and r rational. There is a $\delta > 0$ such that s rational, and $|r - s| < \delta$ implies

$$|a^r - a^s| = a^r\,|1 - a^{s-r}| < \epsilon\, a^r.$$

There are then rational numbers r_1, r_2, s_1, s_2, with $r_1 < x < s_1$, $r_2 < y < s_2$, such that

$$a^{s_1+s_2} - a^{r_1+r_2} < \epsilon \cdot a^{r_1+r_2}.$$

Then

$$a^{r_1+r_2} < a^{x+y} < a^{s_1+s_2}$$

and

$$a^{r_1+r_2} < a^x a^y < a^{s_1+s_2},$$

so that

$$|a^{x+y} - a^x a^y| < \epsilon\, a^{x+y}.$$

Since this holds for every $\epsilon > 0$, we have

$$a^{x+y} = a^x a^y.$$

We now show that a^x is continuous everywhere. Let $h \neq 0$. Then

$$a^{x+h} - a^x = a^x(a^h - 1).$$

This implies that

$$\lim_{h\to 0} (a^{x+h} - a^x) = 0, \quad \text{since} \quad \lim_{h\to 0} a^h = 1.$$

Hence, a^x is continuous at x.

Theorem 1

For every $a > 0$, the function a^x is continuous. If $a > 1$, it is strictly increasing; if $a < 1$, it is strictly decreasing.

We have proved the theorem for $a > 1$. The proof for $0 < a < 1$ may be based on this case, since then $1/a > 1$. We leave the proof to the reader. We note that, for $a \neq 1$, the functions a^x are always positive and assume all positive values.

We now consider continuous functions f which satisfy the condition

$$f(x + y) = f(x)f(y)$$

for every real x and y.

The functions a^x, $a > 0$, have this property. We show that, except for the function which is identically zero, they are the only continuous functions with this property.

Let f be such that for every $x, y \in \mathrm{R}$,

$$f(x + y) = f(x)f(y).$$

We first note that this implies $f(1) \geq 0$, since $f(1) = f(1/2)f(1/2) \geq 0$. If $f(1) = 0$, then for every x,

$$f(x) = f((x - 1) + 1) = f(x - 1)f(1) = 0.$$

Suppose, then, that $f(1) = a > 0$. Then, it follows easily that, for every rational r, $f(r) = a^r$. Thus, f agrees with the function a^x, $x \in \mathrm{R}$, on the rationals, and if f is continuous, it is this function. We have thus proved

Theorem 2

If f is continuous, not identically zero, and satisfies

$$f(x + y) = f(x)f(y)$$

for all $x, y \in \mathrm{R}$, there is an $a > 0$ such that

$$f(x) = a^x \quad \textit{for every} \quad x \in \mathrm{R}.$$

3. THE FUNCTION $\log_a x$

Let $a > 1$. The function f defined by

$$f(x) = a^x, \quad x \in \mathrm{R},$$

is strictly increasing, continuous, and assumes all positive values.

The inverse function f^{-1} exists. Its domain is the set of positive reals, it is strictly increasing and continuous. We write this function L as

$$L(x) = f^{-1}(x) = \log_a x, \quad x > 0.$$

We note that for every $x, y \in \mathrm{R}^+$,

$$L(xy) = L(x) + L(y).$$

To show this, let $x = f(u)$, $y = f(v)$. Then

$$xy = f(u)f(v) = f(u + v),$$

so that

$$L(xy) = Lf(u + v) = u + v = L(x) + L(y).$$

In other words,

$$\log_a xy = \log_a x + \log_a y$$

for all $x > 0$, $y > 0$.

The function L has the following properties.

(a) Its domain is the set of positive real numbers.

(b) It is strictly increasing, continuous, and takes on all real values.

(c) $\log_a 1 = 0$.

(d) $\log_a x^y = y \log_a x$.

(e) $\log_x y \log_y z = \log_x z$.

We again consider the converse question. Suppose f is continuous and has the property

$$f(xy) = f(x) + f(y).$$

If $f(0)$ were defined, then $f(0) = f(x) + f(0)$, for all x, so that f is identically zero.

Suppose f not identically zero. We have $f(1 \cdot x) = f(x) + f(1)$, so that $f(1) = 0$; moreover, $f(1) = 2f(-1)$, so $f(-1) = 0$. We next note that, for $x \neq 0$, $f(-x) = f(x)$, since $f(-x) = f(-1) + f(x) = f(x)$. For $x \neq 0$, $f(1/x) = -f(x)$, since $f(1/x) + f(x) = f(1) = 0$. We have shown, in the last chapter, that a continuous function on an interval assumes all values between those assumed at the end points. Since $f(1) = 0$ and $f(x^n) = nf(x)$, it then follows that f takes on all real values. There is an $a > 0$ such that $f(a) = 1$. Then $f(a^n) = n$, $f(a^{-n}) = -n$, and $f(a^{1/n}) = 1/n$. It follows that for every rational number $r = m/n$, $f(a^r) = m/n$. But, as r varies over the rationals, a^r varies over a dense set of positive real numbers. It follows that

$$f(x) = \log_a |x|$$

for all x in a dense set, so that

$$f(x) = \log_a |x|.$$

4. ARC LENGTH

Let $I = [a, b]$ be a closed interval, and let

$$f: I \to \mathrm{R}$$

be a continuous function. The graph of the function, or the **curve** which it defines, is the set

$$C = \{[x, f(x)]: x \in I\}.$$

We shall define the length of this curve, which we shall designate by either $l(C)$ or $l(f)$. Let

$$\pi = [a = x_0 < x_1 < \cdots < x_n = b]$$

be a partition of I, and let

$$\lambda(f, \pi) = \sum_{i=1}^{n} \{(x_i - x_{i-1})^2 + [f(x_i) - f(x_{i-1})]^2\}^{1/2}.$$

Then $\lambda(f, \pi)$ is the length of a polygonal curve inscribed in C (or quasi linear function "inscribed" in f).

The **length** of the curve C is defined as

$$l(C) = l(f) = \sup \lambda(f, \pi),$$

for all partitions π of I. If $l(C) < \infty$, the curve is said to be of **finite length.**

We briefly discuss some special classes of functions for which the curve is of finite length.

In the first place, if $f: I = [a, b] \to \mathrm{R}$, is continuous and monotonically nondecreasing, or nonincreasing, it is easy to show that

$$l(f) \leq |f(b) - f(a)| + b - a < \infty.$$

We now introduce an important and interesting class of functions for which the length is finite. A function $f: I \to \mathrm{R}$ is **convex** if for every $a \leq x_1 < x_2 \leq b$,

$$f(kx_1 + (1 - k)x_2) \leq kf(x_1) + (1 - k)f(x_2),$$

whenever $0 \leq k \leq 1$.

Theorem 3

If $f: I = [a, b] \to \mathrm{R}$, is convex then f is continuous on $J = (a, b)$ and its values at a and b may be changed, if necessary, so that it is continuous on I.

Proof

Let $x \in J$ and suppose f is not continuous at x. There are sequences $\{x_n\}$, $\{y_n\}$ converging to x with $\{f(x_n)\}$, $\{f(y_n)\}$ converging to different values, where $\pm\infty$ are allowed. There are then $u < v < w$ with $[v, f(v)]$ above the line segment joining $[u, f(u)]$ to $[w, f(w)]$. ∎

We now indicate a proof of the fact that a convex function has finite length without giving all the details.

(a) If f is convex, then every quasilinear function inscribed in f is convex. We leave the proof to the reader.

(b) If f is quasilinear and convex, then its graph is made up of consecutive line segments. The slopes of these segments increase as we move to the right.

(c) If $f: I = [a, b] \to R$ is convex, there is a $\xi \in I$ such that f is monotonically nonincreasing on $[a, \xi]$ and monotonically nondecreasing on $[\xi, b]$.

It is easy to see that otherwise there is an inscribed quasilinear function in f which is not convex.

The fact that $f: I \to R$ is convex implies $l(f) < \infty$ is now obvious.

5. THE TRIGONOMETRIC FUNCTIONS

Consider the function

$$f: [-1, 1] \to R$$

defined by $f(x) = (1 - x^2)^{1/2}$. The curve corresponding to this function is the upper half of the unit circle.

Let $-1 \leq x \leq 1$ and let $s = s(x)$ be the length of f on $[x, 1]$. Then let

$$\sin s = \sin s(x) = f(x).$$

This defines $\sin s$ for all nonnegative s not greater than the length of the semicircle of radius 1. This length is obviously finite and is designated as π.

By proceeding from the point $(1, 0)$ on the circle $x^2 + y^2 = 1$ and letting s be the length of arc traversed if the rotation is counterclockwise and the negative of the length of arc traversed if the rotation is clockwise, we may define $\sin s$ for all real values of s as the y coordinate of the terminal point P.

It follows that $|\sin s| \leq 1$ for all s, $\sin (s + 2\pi) = \sin s$ for all x, and $|\sin s - \sin t| \leq |s - t|$ for all $s, t \in R$. We prove

$$\lim_{\substack{s \to 0 \\ s \neq 0}} \frac{\sin s}{s} = 1$$

Let (x, y) be a point on the first quadrant arc of the circle $x^2 + y^2 = 1$, and s the length of the arc joining (x, y) to $(1, 0)$. Then the function $f(x) = (1 - x^2)^{1/2}$ is decreasing on the interval $[x, 1]$. So,

$$\sin s = y \leq s \leq y + (1 - x) = \sin s + (1 - x)$$

and, for $x \neq 1$,

$$1 \leq \frac{s}{\sin s} \leq 1 + \frac{1 - x}{(1 - x^2)^{1/2}}.$$

Now, for

$$x \neq 1, \qquad (1 - x)^2/(1 - x^2) = -1 + \frac{2}{1 + x}$$

so that

$$\lim_{x \to 1} \frac{1 - x}{(1 - x^2)^{1/2}} = 0.$$

The cosine function is defined so that $\cos s$ is the x coordinate of the point P whose y coordinate is $\sin s$. Thus $\cos s$ is defined for all s. The reader may easily derive many interesting properties of these and the other related trigonometric functions.

EXERCISES

1.1 If f is lower semicontinuous and $f(x + y) = f(x) + f(y)$, for all x and y, show that f is linear.

2.1 Consider the function x^a, a real, $x > 0$.
(a) Prove the function is continuous.
(b) If $a > 0$, prove the function is increasing.
(c) If $a < 0$, prove the function is decreasing.

2.2 Discuss the various possibilities for $x \leq 0$.

2.3 Prove Theorem 1 for $0 < a < 1$.

3.1 If a, b, and c are positive real numbers, show that

$$\log_b a \log_c b = \log_c a.$$

4.1 Find the length of the upper half of the ellipse $x^2 + 2y^2 = 1$, correct to 2 decimals.

4.2 Prove that if f is convex, every quasilinear function inscribed in f is convex.

4.3 Show that if f is quasilinear and convex, the slopes of the segments which make up its graph increase as we move to the right.

4.4 If f is convex on $[a, b]$, show there is a $\xi \in [a, b]$ such that f is monotonically nonincreasing on $[a, \xi]$ and monotonically nondecreasing on $[\xi, b]$.

5.1 Prove that

$$\lim_{x \to 0} \frac{1 - \cos x}{x} = 0.$$

CHAPTER 6

SEQUENCES AND SERIES OF FUNCTIONS

1. CONVERGENT SEQUENCES AND SERIES

Let $S \subset R$. A **sequence** $\{f_n\}$ **of functions** on S associates, with each $n \in N$, a function

$$f_n\colon S \to R.$$

Thus, a sequence of functions on S is a mapping of the set N of natural numbers into the set of real functions on S. We call S the **domain** of the sequence of functions. We give two examples.

Example A Let $f_n(x) = x^n$, $n = 1, 2, \cdots$, $x \in R$. Then $\{f_n\}$ is a sequence of functions on R.

Example B Let $f_n(x) = x/n$, $n = 1, 2, \cdots$, $x \in R$.

In both cases we have sequences whose domain is the set of all real numbers.

A sequence $\{f_n\}$ of functions on a set $S \subset R$ is said to **converge** to a function f on S if, for every $x \in S$,

$$f(x) = \lim_n f_n(x).$$

The question of convergence of a sequence of functions reduces to the convergence of sequences of numbers. Thus, for any $x \in S$, $\{f_n\}$

converges at x if the sequence $\{f_n(x)\}$ of numbers converges. Convergence on S merely means convergence at every $x \in S$.

In Example A above, the sequence $\{x^n\}$ does not converge at $x = -1$, nor does it converge at any x for which $|x| > 1$. However, if we let, $I = (-1, 1]$, then if we let $f_n(x) = x^n$, $n = 1, 2, \cdots$, the sequence converges to $f(x) = 0$ on $(-1, 1)$, and $f(1) = 1$.

In Example B, the sequence $\{x/n\}$ converges to $f(x) = 0$ on R.

We give several further examples. Some of these will have interesting properties which elucidate ideas introduced later in the text.

Example C Let $f_n: \mathrm{R} \to \mathrm{R}$ be defined by $f_n(x) = nx/(1 + n^2x^2)$, $n = 1, 2, \cdots$. For $x = 0$, the sequence $\{f_n(0)\}$ converges to 0.

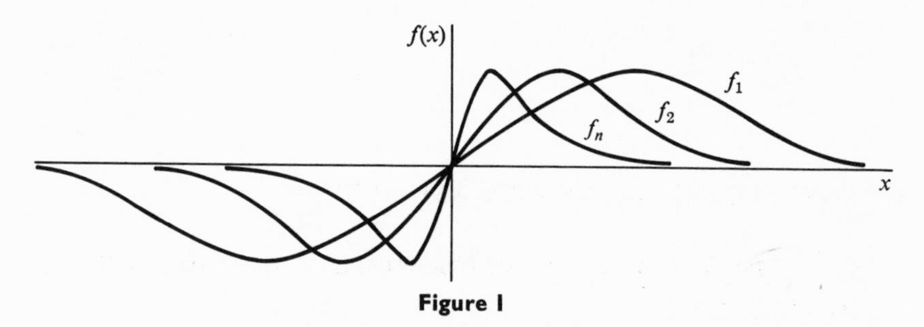

Figure I

Let $x \neq 0$. Let $\epsilon > 0$ and $N > 1/(\epsilon\,|x|)$. Then $n > N$ implies

$$\left|\frac{nx}{1 + n^2x^2}\right| < \frac{1}{n\,|x|} < \frac{1}{N\,|x|} < \epsilon.$$

Hence $\{f_n\}$ converges everywhere to the function $f(x) = 0$.

However, for every n, there is an x, i.e., $x = 1/n$, for which $f_n(x) = 1/2$. Indeed,

$$f_n\left(\frac{1}{n}\right) = \frac{1}{1 + 1} = \frac{1}{2}.$$

Moreover, this is the maximum value of $f_n(x)$. To show this, let $x_n = 1/n + h$, $h \neq 0$. Then,

$$f_n(x) = \frac{1 + nh}{2 + 2nh + n^2h^2} < \frac{1}{2}.$$

The graphs of the functions are indicated in Figure 1.

We shall see later on that, while this sequence converges, it does not converge uniformly in a sense to be defined.

The next example gives an idea of the vast class of functions which may be obtained by starting with continuous functions and taking repeated limits.

Example D For every n, let f_n: R $\to$ R be defined by

$$f_n(x) = (\cos m!\, \pi x)^{2n},$$

where m is a fixed natural number. Then

$$|\cos m!\, \pi x| = 1$$

if and only if x is a rational number for which $m!\, x$ is an integer. Let A_m be this set of rational numbers.

It should be clear that $\{f_n\}$ converges to the function g defined by

$$g(x) = \begin{cases} 1, & x \in A_m \\ 0, & x \notin A_m. \end{cases}$$

We note that

$$A_1 \subset A_2 \subset \cdots \subset A_m \subset \cdots$$

and

$$\text{Q} = \bigcup_{m=1}^{\infty} A_m,$$

where Q is the set of rational numbers.

Let $\{g_m\}$ be the sequence of functions defined by

$$g_m(x) = \begin{cases} 1, & x \in A_m \\ 0, & x \notin A_m. \end{cases}$$

Then $\{g_m\}$ converges to the function f, which is 1 at the rationals and 0 at the irrationals.

We may accordingly write the formula

$$f(x) = \lim_{m\to\infty} \lim_{n\to\infty} (\cos m!\, \pi x)^{2n}.$$

We turn now to a consideration of series of functions. The definitions of series of functions, and of convergent series of functions, depend on those of sequences of functions.

Thus, a series $\sum_{n=1}^{\infty} f_n$ of functions converges on a set S if the corresponding sequence $\{s_n\}$ converges on S, where

$$s_n = f_1 + \cdots + f_n, \qquad n = 1, 2, \cdots.$$

Example E Consider the series

$$1 + x + \frac{x^2}{2!} + \cdots + \frac{x^n}{n!} + \cdots$$

defined for all $x \in \mathrm{R}$.

For any $x \neq 0$, the magnitude of the ratio of the $(n + 1)$st term to the nth term is $|x|/n$. Since this ratio converges to 0, the series converges for every x. We show that it converges to the function e^x.

Since the series converges absolutely, for every x, we may arrange the formal product

$$\left(1 + x + \frac{x^2}{2!} + \cdots\right)\left(1 + y + \frac{y^2}{2!} + \cdots\right)$$

is any order. For each $n = 0, 1, 2, \cdots$, consider all terms for which the sum of the powers of x and y is n. We obtain for this sum

$$\begin{aligned}
&\frac{x^n}{n!} + \frac{x^{n-1}y}{(n-1)!} + \frac{x^{n-2}y^2}{(n-2)!\,2!} + \cdots + \frac{y^n}{n!} \\
&= \frac{1}{n!}\left(x^n + nx^{n-1}y + \frac{n(n-1)}{2!}x^{n-2}y^2 + \cdots + y^n\right) \\
&= \frac{1}{n!}(x + y)^n.
\end{aligned}$$

It follows that

$$\begin{aligned}
&\left(1 + x + \frac{x^2}{2!} + \cdots\right)\left(1 + y + \frac{y^2}{2!} + \cdots\right) \\
&\qquad = 1 + (x + y) + \frac{(x + y)^2}{2!} + \cdots.
\end{aligned}$$

In other words, if the function to which the series converges is f, then for every x, y,

$$f(x + y) = f(x) + f(y).$$

We know that $f(1) = e$. It follows that $f(x) = e^x$ for rational x. Since it is clear that f is increasing for positive values, and e^x is continuous, it follows that $f(x) = e^x$ for all x.

2. UNIFORM CONVERGENCE

In Example A above, the sequence $\{x^n\}$, defined on $[0, 1]$, is a sequence of continuous functions which converges to the function f given by

$$f(x) = \begin{cases} 0 & x \neq 1 \\ 1 & x = 1. \end{cases}$$

The limit function is thus discontinuous at $x = 1$.

Thus continuity, as well as other important properties of functions, to be discussed later, are not preserved by convergence. There is a stronger form of convergence which allows us to cope with some of these difficulties.

A sequence $\{f_n\}$ of functions, defined on a set S, is said to **converge uniformly** to a function f on S if, for every $\epsilon > 0$, there is an N such that, for every $x \in S$ and $n > N$,

$$|f(x) - f_n(x)| < \epsilon.$$

Example A The sequence $\{x^n\}$ converges on $[0, 1]$ to the function f for which $f(x) = 0$, $x \neq 1$ and $f(1) = 1$. We show that the convergence is not uniform. Let $\epsilon = 1/2$. For every n, let $x_n = 2^{-1/n}$. Then $x_n^n = 1/2$ so that $|f_n(x_n) - f(x_n)| = 1/2$.

On the other hand, this sequence of functions converges uniformly on every interval $[0, k]$, $0 < k < 1$. Accordingly, let $\epsilon > 0$ and let $N > \dfrac{\log \epsilon}{\log k}$. Then $x \in [0, k]$ and $n > N$ implies

$$|x^n| \leq k^n < k^N < k^{\frac{\log \epsilon}{\log k}} = \epsilon.$$

Example B The sequence $\{x/n\}$ converges to 0, for every $x \in \mathrm{R}$, so that it converges to the function f, which is identically 0. However, the convergence is not uniform. If $S \subset \mathrm{R}$ is bounded, then the convergence is uniform on S. We leave the proofs to the reader.

Example C Let $f_n\colon \mathrm{R} \to \mathrm{R}$ be defined by

$$f_n(x) = \frac{nx}{1 + n^2x^2}, \qquad n = 1, 2, \cdots.$$

We showed that this sequence converges to the zero function. However, we showed that, for every n, $f_n(1/n) = 1/2$, so that the convergence is not uniform. Let $S = [x: |x| > k > 0]$. We now show that the convergence is uniform on S. Since $f_n(-x) = -f_n(x)$, for every n and x, we may assume $x > 0$. Then

$$f_n(x) = \frac{nx}{1 + n^2x^2} < \frac{1}{nx} \leq \frac{1}{nk}$$

for all $x \geq k$. Let $\epsilon > 0$. There is an N such that $1/(Nk) < \epsilon$. Then, for every $n > N$ and $x \geq k$, $f_n(x) < \epsilon$.

A series $\sum_{n=1}^{\infty} f_n$ is said to **converge uniformly** on a set S if the associated sequence of partial sums converges uniformly on S. A series $\sum_{n=1}^{\infty} f_n$ is said to **converge absolutely uniformly** on S if the associated sequence of partial sums of the series $\sum_{n=1}^{\infty} |f_n|$ converges uniformly on S.

It is easy to see that $\sum_{n=1}^{\infty} f_n$ converges uniformly on S if and only if, for every $\epsilon > 0$, there is an N such that $n > N$ and $p > 0$ implies that, for every $x \in S$,

$$|f_{n+1}(x) + \cdots + f_{n+p}(x)| < \epsilon.$$

It converges absolutely uniformly on S if and only if, for every $\epsilon > 0$, there is an N such that $n > N$ and $p > 0$ implies that, for every $x \in S$,

$$|f_{n+1}(x)| + \cdots + |f_{n+p}(x)| < \epsilon.$$

Example D We show that the series

$$1 + x + \frac{x^2}{2!} + \cdots + \frac{x^n}{n!} + \cdots$$

does not converge uniformly on R, but for every M, converges absolutely uniformly on the set $S = [x: |x| \leq M]$.

Proof

For every n, there is an x such that $\frac{x^n}{n!} > 1$ so that the series does not converge uniformly.

For every $M > 0$, and $\epsilon > 0$, there is an N such that $n > N$ and

$p > 0$ implies

$$\frac{M^{n+1}}{(n+1)!} + \cdots + \frac{M^{n+p}}{(n+p)!} < \epsilon,$$

so that the convergence on S is absolutely uniform. ∎

3. CONTINUOUS FUNCTIONS

We have seen that a sequence of continuous functions can converge to a function which is not continuous. For example, $\{x^n\}$ converges on $[0, 1]$ to a function which is not continuous at $x = 1$.

However, we have

Theorem 1

If $\{f_n\}$ is a sequence of functions which converges uniformly to a function f on a set S, and f_n is continuous at $x_0 \in S$, $n = 1, 2, \cdots$, then f is continuous at x_0.

Proof

Let $\epsilon > 0$. There is an N such that $n > N$ and $x \in S$ implies $|f(x) - f_n(x)| < \epsilon/3$. Let $n > N$. There is a $\delta > 0$ such that $x \in S$ and $|x - x_0| < \delta$ implies $|f_n(x) - f_n(x_0)| < \epsilon/3$. Let $x \in S$ and $|x - x_0| < \delta$. Then $|f(x) - f(x_0)| \le |f(x) - f_n(x)| + |f_n(x) - f_n(x_0)| + |f_n(x_0) - f(x_0)| < \epsilon/3 + \epsilon/3 + \epsilon/3 = \epsilon$. ∎

We have had examples of sequences of continuous functions which converge (but not uniformly) to a function which is not continuous. On the other hand, it is not necessary for a sequence of continuous functions to converge uniformly if it is to converge to a continuous function. For example, we have seen that the sequence $\{nx/(1 + n^2x^2)\}$ converges to the zero function, but not uniformly.

On the other hand, there are certain conditions under which convergence implies uniform convergence.

A sequence $\{f_n\}$ of functions defined on a set S is said to be **monotonically nonincreasing** if, for every n and $x \in S$,

$$f_{n+1}(x) \le f_n(x).$$

Theorem 2

If S is compact and $\{f_n\}$ is a monotonically nonincreasing sequence of continuous functions on S, which converges to a function f which is continuous on S, the convergence is uniform.

Proof

Let $g_n = f_n - f$, $n = 1, 2, \cdots$. Then $\{g_n\}$ is monotonically nonincreasing and converges to zero on S. We need only show that $\{g_n\}$ converges uniformly to zero on S.

Let $\epsilon > 0$. For every $x \in S$, there is an $n(x)$ such that $g_{n(x)}(x) < \epsilon/2$. Since $g_{n(x)}$ is continuous, there is an open interval J_x, with $x \in J_x$, such that $y \in S \cap J_x$ implies $g_{n(x)}(y) < g_{n(x)}(x) + \epsilon/2 < \epsilon$. The collection

$$\mathscr{J} = [J_x \colon x \in S]$$

covers S, and since S is compact, a finite subset $J_{x_1}, \cdots, J_{x_r}$ of $\mathscr{J}$ covers S. Let

$$N = \max\,[n(x_1), \cdots, n(x_r)].$$

Then $g_N(x) < \epsilon$ for every $x \in S$. Since $\{g_n\}$ is monotonically nonincreasing, $n > N$ and $x \in S$ implies $g_n(x) < \epsilon$, so that the sequence $\{g_n\}$ converges uniformly to zero on S. ∎

4. WEIERSTRASS POLYNOMIAL APPROXIMATION

We prove a famous theorem of K. Weierstrass which says that if f is continuous on a closed interval I, there is a sequence $\{p_n\}$ of polynomials which converges uniformly to f on I. Results of the last chapter may be interpreted to say that continuous functions are uniform limits of sequences of step functions or of quasilinear functions.

We shall give a proof of the Weierstrass theorem in which a formula is given for the approximating polynomials. This proof was discovered by S. Bernstein, and the polynomials used are called Bernstein polynomials.

For every $n = 0, 1, \cdots$ and $k = 0, \cdots, n$ let

$$p_{nk}(x) = \binom{n}{k} x^k (1 - x)^{n-k}$$

where $\binom{n}{k} = C(n, k) = \dfrac{n!}{k!\,(n-k)!}$ is the number of combinations of n things taken k at a time. Then p_{nk} is a polynomial of degree n. It has the following probabilistic interpretation. For each $x \in [0, 1]$, if x is the probability of an event, then

$$p_{nk}(x) = \binom{n}{k} x^k (1 - x)^{n-k}$$

is the probability that the event will occur exactly k times in n independent trials. Although we shall derive all needed relations by means of direct computation, it is worth mentioning that from elementary probability theory we have

(a) $\sum_{k=0}^{n} p_{nk}(x) = \sum_{k=0}^{n} \binom{n}{k} x^k(1-x)^{n-k} = 1,$

for every n and $x \in [0, 1]$.

(b) $\sum_{k=0}^{n} kp_{nk}(x) = \sum_{k=0}^{n} k\binom{n}{k} x^k(1-x)^{n-k} = nx$

for every n and $x \in [0, 1]$.

(c) $\sum_{k=0}^{n} (nx-k)^2 p_{nk}(x) = nx(1-x),$

for every $x \in [0, 1]$.

For **(a)**, by the binomial theorem,

$$\sum_{k=0}^{n} \binom{n}{k} x^k(1-x)^{n-k} = [x + (1-x)]^n = 1.$$

For **(b)**, note that $k\binom{n}{k} = n\binom{n-1}{k-1}$, $k = 1, 2, \cdots, n$. Thus,

$$\sum_{k=0}^{n} k\binom{n}{k} x^k(1-x)^{n-k} = \sum_{k=1}^{n} k\binom{n}{k} x^k(1-x)^{n-k}$$

$$= \sum_{k=1}^{n} n\binom{n-1}{k-1} x^k(1-x)^{n-k} = nx\sum_{k=0}^{n-1} \binom{n-1}{k} x^k(x-1)^{n-1-k} = nx.$$

For **(c)**, it is clear that it is easier to compute

$\sum_{k=0}^{n} k(k-1)\binom{n}{k} x^k(1-x)^{n-k}$. This expression is equal to

$$\sum_{k=2}^{n} n(n-1)x^2\binom{n-2}{k-2} x^{k-2}(1-x)^{n-k} = n(n-1)x^2.$$

Now,

$$\sum_{k=0}^{n} (nx-k)^2 p_{nk}(x) = \sum_{k=0}^{n} n^2x^2 p_{nk}(x) - 2nx\sum_{k=0}^{n} kp_{nk}(x)$$

$$+ \sum_{k=0}^{n} k(k-1)p_{nk}(x) + \sum_{k=0}^{n} kp_{nk}(x)$$

$$= n^2x^2 - 2n^2x^2 + n(n-1)x^2 + nx = nx(1-x).$$

We shall need, along with **(a)**, **(b)**, **(c)**, the fact that $x(1 - x) \leq 1/4$ for all $x \in [0, 1]$. We now define the Bernstein polynomials by

$$B_n(f, x) = \sum_{k=0}^{n} f\left(\frac{k}{n}\right) p_{nk}(x),$$

for every f: $[0, 1] \to R$, and $n = 0, 1, 2, \cdots$.

We prove

Theorem 3

If f is continuous on $[0, 1]$, *then* $\{B_n\}$ *converges uniformly to f on* $[0, 1]$.

Proof

For every n,

$$|f(x) - B_n(f, x)| = \left| f(x) - \sum_{k=0}^{n} f\left(\frac{k}{n}\right) p_{nk}(x) \right|$$

$$= \left| \sum_{k=0}^{n} \left\{ f(x) - f\left(\frac{k}{n}\right) \right\} p_{nk}(x) \right| \leq \sum_{k=0}^{n} \left| f(x) - f\left(\frac{k}{n}\right) \right| p_{kn}(x).$$

Let M be such that $|f(x)| \leq \dfrac{M}{2}$ for all $x \in [0, 1]$. Choose $\epsilon > 0$, and let $\delta > 0$ be such that $|x - y| < \delta$, $x, y \in [0, 1]$, implies $|f(x) - f(y)| < \dfrac{\epsilon}{2}$. Now, for every $n = 1, 2, \cdots$, and $x \in [0, 1]$,

$$|f(x) - B_n(f, x)| \leq \sum_{|x - k/n| < \delta} \left| f(x) - f\left(\frac{k}{n}\right) \right| p_{nk}(x)$$

$$+ \sum_{|x} \left| f(x) - f\left(\frac{k}{n}\right) \right| p_{nk}(x) \leq \frac{\epsilon}{2} + M \sum_{|x - k/n \leq \delta} p_{nk}(x)$$

$$\leq \frac{\epsilon}{2} + M \sum_{|x - k/n| \geq \delta} \frac{(nx - k)^2}{n^2 \delta^2} p_{nk}(x)$$

$$\leq \frac{\epsilon}{2} + \frac{M}{n^2 \delta^2} \sum_{k=0}^{n} (nx - k)^2 p_{nk}(x)$$

$$= \frac{\epsilon}{2} + \frac{Mx(1 - x)}{n\delta^2} \leq \frac{\epsilon}{2} + \frac{M}{4n\delta^2}.$$

Let N be such that $\dfrac{M}{4N\delta^2} < \dfrac{\epsilon}{2}$.

Then, for every $n > N$ and $x \in [0, 1]$, $|f(x) - B_n(f, x)| < \epsilon$. It follows that $\{B_n\}$ converges uniformly to f on $[0, 1]$. ∎

Corollary 1

If $[a, b]$ *is any closed interval and* f *is continuous on* $[a, b]$, *there is a sequence* $\{p_n\}$ *of polynomials which converges uniformly to* f *on* $[a, b]$.

Corollary 2

If $f: R \to \mathrm{R}$ *is continuous, there is a sequence of polynomials which converges to* f *on* R, *the convergence being uniform on every compact set.*

The proofs of the corollaries are left to the reader.

5. EQUICONTINUITY

A set $F = [f]$ of functions, defined on a set S, is said to be **uniformly bounded** if there is an M such that, for every $f \in F$ and $x \in S$, $|f(x)| \leq M$. A sequence $\{f_n\}$ is said to be uniformly bounded on a set S if there is an M such that $|f_n(x)| \leq M$ for every $n = 1, 2, \cdots$ and every $x \in S$.

We have seen that there are uniformly bounded sequences which do not converge uniformly. For example, the sequence $\{x^n\}$ does not converge uniformly on $[0, 1]$, nor does any subsequence converge uniformly on this interval.

It is important, for proving the existence of solutions of certain differential equations, to have conditions under which a sequence of functions has a uniformly convergent subsequence. We now give such a condition.

We say that a sequence $\{f_n\}$ of functions, defined on a set S, is **uniformly equicontinuous** on S if, for every $\epsilon > 0$ there is a $\delta > 0$ such that $x, y \in S$ and $|x - y| < \delta$ implies $|f_n(x) - f_n(y)| < \epsilon$, for every n.

We prove

Theorem 4

If $\{f_n\}$ *is uniformly bounded and uniformly equicontinuous on a closed interval* $I = [a, b]$, *then* $\{f_n\}$ *has a subsequence which converges uniformly on* $[a, b]$.

Proof

Let $\{r_n\}$ be the rationals in $[a, b]$ ordered as a sequence. The first part of the proof is to show that $\{f_n\}$ has a subsequence which converges at every r_n, $n = 1, 2, \cdots$. The sequence $\{f_n(r_1)\}$ is a bounded sequence of numbers, so that it has a convergent subsequence, which we shall write as $\{f_{1n}(r_1)\}$. Thus the subsequence $\{f_{1n}\}$ of $\{f_n\}$ converges at r_1.

Now, $\{f_{1n}(r_2)\}$ is a bounded sequence of real numbers, so that it has a convergent subsequence $\{f_{2n}(r_2)\}$. Thus the subsequence $\{f_{2n}\}$ of $\{f_{1n}\}$ converges at r_2. By induction, we obtain a sequence of sequences,

$$(*) \qquad \begin{array}{l} f_1 = f_{01}, f_2 = f_{02}, \cdots, f_n = f_{0n} \cdots \\ f_{11}, f_{12}, \cdots, f_{1n}, \cdots \\ f_{21}, f_{22}, \cdots, f_{2n}, \cdots \\ \cdot\cdot\cdot\cdot\cdot \\ f_{m1}, f_{m2}, \cdots, f_{mn}, \cdots \\ \cdot\cdot\cdot\cdot\cdot \end{array}$$

For every m, $\{f_{mn}\}$ is a subsequence of $\{f_{m-1,n}\}$ which converges at r_m. It follows that $\{f_{mn}\}$ converges at $r_1, r_2, \cdots, r_m$. We want a subsequence of $\{f_n\}$ which converges at $r_1, r_2, \cdots. r_m, \cdots$. The diagonal sequence of the array (*) does the job.

We show that the subsequence $\{f_{mm}\}$ of $\{f_n\}$ converges at every rational in $[a, b]$. Let r_k be a rational in $[a, b]$. Then $f_{kk}, f_{k+1,k+1}, \cdots$ is a subsequence of $f_{k1}, f_{k2}, \cdots, f_{kn}, \cdots$ so that $\{f_{mm}(r_k)\}$ converges.

We have used only the fact that the sequence $\{f_n\}$ is bounded at each rational to show that there is a subsequence $\{g_n = f_{nn}\}$ of $\{f_n\}$ which converges at each rational in $[a, b]$. Since $\{f_n\}$ is uniformly equicontinuous, this is also true of $\{g_n\}$.

We prove that $\{g_n\}$ converges uniformly on $[a, b]$. Let $\epsilon > 0$. There is a $\delta > 0$ such that $x, y \in [a, b]$, $|x - y| < \delta$, implies $|g_n(x) - g_n(y)| < \epsilon$, for every n. Let $r_1 < r_2 < \cdots < r_t$ be rationals such that

$$\max(r_1 - a, r_2 - r_1, \cdots, b - r_t) < \delta.$$

For each $i = 1, \cdots, t$, there is an N_i such that $m, n > N_i$ implies $|g_n(r_i) - g_m(r_i)| < \epsilon$. Let $N = \max(N_1, N_2, \cdots, N_t)$. Let $n, m > N$ and $x \in [a, b]$. There is an i such that $|x - r_i| < \delta$. Then

$$\begin{aligned} |g_n(x) - g_m(x)| &\le |g_n(x) - g_n(r_i)| + |g_n(r_i) - g_m(r_i)| \\ &+ |g_m(r_i) - g_m(x)| < \epsilon + \epsilon + \epsilon = 3\epsilon. \end{aligned}$$

Thus $\{g_n\}$ converges uniformly on $[a, b]$.

We prove an analogous theorem for sequences of functions, which are uniformly bounded, with each function monotonically nondecreasing. So, let $\{f_n\}$ be a sequence of functions defined on $I = [a, b]$, each of which is monotonically nondecreasing. Suppose $|f_n(x)| \leq M$ for all $x \in I$ and $n = 1, 2, \cdots$.

As above, if $D \subset I$ is a countable dense set in I, there is a subsequence $\{g_n\}$ of $\{f_n\}$ which converges on D to a function g. Now $g: D \to \mathrm{R}$. We show that g is monotonically nondecreasing. Let $x, y \in D$, $x < y$. For $\epsilon > 0$, there is an n such that $|g(x) - g_n(x)| < \epsilon$ and $|g(y) - g_n(y)| < \epsilon$. But,

$$g(x) - \epsilon < g_n(x) \leq g_n(y) < g(y) + \epsilon.$$

So, $g(x) < g(y) + 2\epsilon$. Since this holds for every $\epsilon > 0$, it follows that $g(x) \leq g(y)$.

We extend the definition of g to the semiopen interval $(a, b]$. For every $x \in (a, b]$, let

$$g(x) = \sup\,[g(y): y \in D, y \leq x].$$

Then g is monotonically nondecreasing and, for every $x \in D$, $g(x) = \lim_n g_n(x)$.

Since g is monotonically nondecreasing, it is continuous everywhere except at a countable set of points. Let $x \in (a, b]$ be a point of continuity of g. Let $\epsilon > 0$. There are $u < x < v$, with $u, v \in D$, such that $g(u) \leq g(x) \leq g(v) < g(u) + \epsilon$. There is an N such that $n > N$ implies

$$|g(u) - g_n(u)| < \epsilon \quad \text{and} \quad |g(v) - g_n(v)| < \epsilon.$$

Then

$$\begin{aligned}
|g(x) - g_n(x)| &\leq |g(x) - g(u)| + |g(u) - g_n(u)| + |g_n(u) - g_n(x)| \\
&\leq |g(x) - g(u)| + |g(u) - g_n(u)| + |g_n(u) - g_n(v)| \\
&\leq |g(x) - g(u)| + |g(u) - g_n(u)| + |g_n(u) - g(u)| \\
&\quad + |g(u) - g(v)| + |g(v) - g_n(v)| < 5\epsilon.
\end{aligned}$$

Hence, $g(x) = \lim_n g_n(x)$.

We thus have a subsequence $\{g_n\}$ of $\{f_n\}$ which converges everywhere on $[a, b]$, except at a countable set S. By the same diagonalization process as used before, $\{g_n\}$ has a subsequence $\{h_n\}$ which converges at every point of S. Thus $\{h_n\}$ converges everywhere on $[a, b]$. We thus have

Theorem 5

If I is a closed interval and $\{f_n\}$ is a uniformly bounded sequence of functions defined on I, each of which is monotonically nondecreasing, then $\{f_n\}$ has a subsequence which converges everywhere on I.

EXERCISES

1.1 Give an example of a sequence of continuous functions which is not uniformly bounded but converges to zero everywhere.

1.2 Show that if $f(x) = g(x)$, for every x in a dense set, then if f is continuous and g is nondecreasing it follows that $f = g$ everywhere.

1.3 Show that for every $x > 1$, the series

$$\frac{1}{x+1} + \frac{2}{x^2+1} + \frac{4}{x^4+1} + \frac{8}{x^8+1} + \cdots$$

converges to the function $\dfrac{1}{x-1}$.

2.1 Discuss the uniform convergence of the series in Exercise 1.3.

2.2 Give an example of a sequence of continuous functions which converges everywhere but not uniformly on any interval.

2.3 Discuss the convergence and uniform convergence of the sequence

$$\{e^{-nx^2}\}.$$

2.4 Give an example of a sequence of functions which converges on an infinite set S, but does not converge uniformly on any infinite subset of S.

2.5 Show that the sequence $\{x/n\}$ does not converge uniformly on the set of all reals, but converges uniformly on every bounded set.

2.6 If $\sum_{n=1}^{\infty} f_n$ converges uniformly on $[a, b]$ and g is bounded, show that $\sum_{n=1}^{\infty} gf_n$ converges uniformly.

2.7 Discuss the convergence and uniform convergence of $\sum_{n=1}^{\infty} \dfrac{1}{n^x}$ on $1 < x < \infty$.

2.8 Discuss the convergence and uniform convergence of the series

$$\sum_{n=1}^{\infty} \frac{1}{n} \sin nx.$$

3.1 A sequence $\{f_n\}$ of functions is said to be continuously convergent at x_0 to f if, for every $\epsilon > 0$ there is a $\delta > 0$ and an N, such that $n > N$ and $|x - x_0| < \delta$ implies $|f_n(x) - f(x)| < \epsilon$. Show that if a sequence $\{f_n\}$ of continuous functions at x_0 converges continuously to f at x_0 then f is continuous at x_0.

3.2 If $\{f_n\}$ is a nondecreasing sequence of continuous functions, which is bounded at each point, the limit function

$$f = \lim_n f_n$$

is lower semicontinuous.

3.3 Give an example of a sequence of continuous functions which converges everywhere but whose limit is neither upper semicontinuous nor lower semicontinuous.

3.4 Give an example of a sequence of continuous functions which converges everywhere but whose limit is neither upper semicontinuous nor lower semicontinuous on any interval.

3.5 Give an example of a sequence of lower semicontinuous functions which converges to a function which is not the limit of any sequence of continuous functions.

4.1 Show that if $[a, b]$ is any closed interval and f is continuous on $[a, b]$, there is a sequence $\{p_n\}$ of polynomials which converges uniformly to f on $[a, b]$.

4.2 Give an example of a continuous function f on the reals such that no sequence of polynomials converges uniformly to f.

4.3 For every continuous function f on the reals, show that there is a sequence of polynomials which converges to f, the convergence being uniform on every bounded set.

4.4 If f is continuous on $[0, 1]$ and $f(0) = f(1) = 0$, show that there is a sequence $\{p_n\}$ of polynomials, with $p_n(0) = p_n(1) = 0$, $n = 1, 2, \cdots$, which converges uniformly to f.

4.5 If f is continuous on $[0, 1]$, show that there is an increasing sequence of polynomials which converges uniformly to f.

5.1 If $\{f_n\}$ is a sequence of monotonically nondecreasing functions on $[a, b]$, if f is continuous, and if $\{f_n(x)\}$ converges to $f(x)$ for every x in a dense set, show that $\{f_n\}$ converges to f everywhere, and the convergence is uniform.

CHAPTER 7

DIFFERENTIATION

1. DEFINITIONS

We start with a description of the "o" and "O" notations. If f and g are functions, defined either for all x on an interval with 0 as left end point, or for all x on an interval with 0 as right end point, or for all x such that $0 < x < a$, where $a > 0$, we say that

$$f(x) = o(g(x)),$$

as $x \to 0$, if

$$\lim_{x \to 0} \frac{f(x)}{g(x)} = 0.$$

We say that

$$f(x) = O(g(x)),$$

as $x \to 0$, if $f(x)/g(x)$ is bounded in some neighborhood of 0 (with 0 deleted).

The notions $f(x) = o[g(x)]$ and $f(x) = O[g(x)]$ are defined in analogous fashion as $x \to x_0 \neq 0$ or as $x \to +\infty$, or $x \to -\infty$.

In particular, if $\lim_{x \to 0} f(x) = 0$, then $f(x) = o(1)$ as $x \to 0$, and if $f(x)$ is bounded, then $f(x) = O(1)$. If $\lim_{x \to 0} \dfrac{f(x)}{x} = 0$, then $f(x) = o(x)$ as $x \to 0$.

Thus, if we write

$$f(x) = g(x) + o(1) \quad \text{as} \quad x \to 0,$$

we mean

$$\lim_{x \to 0} (f(x) - g(x)) = 0.$$

If we write

$$f(x) = g(x) + o(x) \quad \text{as} \quad x \to 0$$

we mean

$$\lim_{x \to 0} \frac{f(x) - g(x)}{x} = 0.$$

We are now ready to define the derivative of a function at a point. Let $f: I \to R$, where I is an open interval, and let $x_0 \in I$. Then f is said to be **differentiable** at x_0 if there is a constant α such that

$$\frac{f(x_0 + h) - f(x_0)}{h} - \alpha = o(1),$$

as $h \to 0$.

The number α is then called the **derivative** of f at x_0.

It is clear that f is differentiable at x_0 if and only if

$$\lim_{\substack{h \to 0 \\ h \neq 0}} \frac{f(x_0 + h) - f(x_0)}{h}$$

exists, and the limit is the derivative of f at x_0.

It should be clear, from the definition, that f is differentiable at x_0 if and only if the function $f(x_0 + h) - f(x_0)$ of h may be approximated by the linear function αh, as given by the equation

$$f(x_0 + h) - f(x_0) - \alpha h = o(h).$$

The linear function αh is then called the **differential** of f at x_0.

We compare differentiable functions with continuous functions.

(a) If I is an open interval, $f: I \to R$, $x_0 \in I$, and f is differentiable at x_0, then f is continuous at x_0.

Proof

There is an α such that

$$f(x_0 + h) - f(x_0) - \alpha h = o(1).$$

Then $\lim_{h \to 0} (f(x_0 + h) - f(x_0) - \alpha h) = 0$. But $\lim_{h \to 0} \alpha h = 0$. Then

$$\lim_{h \to 0} [f(x_0 + h) - f(x_0)] = 0,$$

so that f is continuous at x_0.

(b) The function $f(x) = |x|$ is continuous at $x = 0$ but is not differentiable there.

If $f\colon I \to \mathrm{R}$, I an open interval, and f is differentiable at every $x \in I$, we obtain a new function $f'\colon I \to \mathrm{R}$, such that at every $x \in I$, $f'(x)$ is the derivative of f at x. The function f' is called the **derivative** of f.

Example A Consider the function $f(x) = x^2$. For every x,

$$\frac{f(x+h) - f(x)}{h} = \frac{(x+h)^2 - x^2}{h} = 2x + h.$$

It follows that $f'(x) = 2x$.

Example B The derivative of $\sin x$ is $\cos x$. In order to show this we first recall that

$$\lim_{h \to 0} \frac{\sin h}{h} = 1,$$

and that $\sin(x + h) = \sin x \cos h + \cos x \sin h$. Then

$$\frac{\sin(x+h) - \sin x}{h} = \cos x \cdot \frac{\sin h}{h} + \sin x \frac{\cos h - 1}{h}.$$

Now

$$\frac{1 - \cos h}{h} = \frac{1 - \cos^2 h}{(1 + \cos h)h} = \sin h \cdot \frac{1}{1 + \cos h} \cdot \frac{\sin h}{h} = o(1)$$

and $\cos x - \cos x \cdot \dfrac{\sin h}{h} = o(1)$, so that

$$\frac{\sin(x+h) - \sin x}{h} = \cos x + o(1).$$

Example C The derivative of e^x is e^x. Now,

$$\frac{e^{x+h} - e^x}{h} = e^x \cdot \frac{e^h - 1}{h}.$$

But

$$e^h = 1 + h + \frac{h^2}{2!} + \cdots,$$

so that

$$\frac{e^{x+h} - e^x}{h} = e^x + e^x\left(\frac{h}{2!} + \frac{h^2}{3!} + \cdots\right).$$

For $|h| < 1$,

$$\left| \frac{h}{2!} + \frac{h^2}{3!} + \cdots \right| < |h|.$$

Thus,

$$\frac{e^{x+h} - e^x}{h} - e^x = o(1).$$

2. THE CLASS OF DIFFERENTIABLE FUNCTIONS

(a) If f and g are differentiable at x, then $f + g$ is differentiable at x, and $(f + g)'(x) = f'(x) + g'(x)$.

Proof

We are given

$$\frac{f(x+h) - f(x)}{h} = f'(x) + \varphi(h)$$

and

$$\frac{g(x+h) - g(x)}{h} = g'(x) + \psi(h)$$

where $\lim_{h \to 0} \varphi(h) = \lim_{h \to 0} \psi(h) = 0$.

Then

$$\frac{f(x+h) + g(x+h) - (f(x) + g(x))}{h} = f'(x) + g'(x) + \varphi(h) + \psi(h)$$

where $\lim_{h \to 0} (\varphi(h) + \psi(h)) = 0$, and the result follows. ∎

(b) If f and g are differentiable at x, then fg is differentiable at x and

$$(fg)'(x) = f(x)g'(x) + g(x)f'(x).$$

Proof

We are given

$$\frac{f(x+h) - f(x)}{h} = f'(x) + \varphi(h)$$

and

$$\frac{g(x+h) - g(x)}{h} = g'(x) + \psi(h),$$

where $\lim_{h \to 0} \varphi(h) = \lim_{h \to 0} \psi(h) = 0$.

Then,

$$\frac{f(x+h)g(x+h)-f(x)g(x)}{h}=\frac{f(x+h)g(x+h)-f(x+h)g(x)}{h}$$

$$+\frac{f(x+h)g(x)-f(x)g(x)}{h}=f(x+h)[g'(x)+\psi(h)]$$

$$+g(x)[f'(x)+\varphi(h)]=f(x)g'(x)+g(x)f'(x)$$

$$+\{(f(x+h)-f(x))g'(x)+f(x+h)\psi(h)+g(x)\varphi(h)\}.$$

Since f is continuous at x, the expression in braces is $o(1)$, and the result follows.

Example A If $f(x) = x$, then $f'(x) = 1$, for every x. Then if $f(x) = x^2$, $f'(x) = x \cdot 1 + 1 \cdot x = 2x$. Suppose that we know that if $f(x) = x^n$, then $f'(x) = nx^{n-1}$. Let $f(x) = x^{n+1} = x \cdot x^n$. Then $f'(x) = 1 \cdot x^n + x \cdot nx^{n-1} = (n+1)x^n$.
We have thus proved that, for every natural number n, the derivative of x^n is nx^{n-1}.

(c) If f is differentiable at x and $f(x) \neq 0$, then $1/f$ is differentiable at x and

$$\left(\frac{1}{f}\right)'(x) = -\frac{f'(x)}{[f(x)]^2}.$$

We leave the proof as an exercise for the reader.

We now prove the so-called **chain rule** for differentiation.

(d) If f and g are differentiable, f at x and g at $f(x)$, then $g \circ f$ is differentiable at x, and

$$(g \circ f)'(x) = g'[f(x)]f'(x).$$

Proof

Suppose there is an $h_o > 0$ such that $0 < |h| < h_o$ implies $f(x+h) \neq f(x)$. Then, for $0 < |h| < h_o$,

$$\frac{(g \circ f)(x+h)-(g \circ f)(x)}{h}=\frac{g[f(x+h)]-g[f(x)]}{h}$$

$$=\frac{g[f(x+h)]-g[f(x)]}{f(x+h)-f(x)}\,\frac{f(x+h)-f(x)}{h}$$

$$=\{g'[f(x)]+\varphi[f(x+h)-f(x)]\}\{f'(x)+\psi(h)\},$$

where $\lim_{h\to 0}\varphi(h) = 0$ and $\lim_{h\to 0}\psi(h) = 0$.

Then

$$\frac{(g \circ f)(x+h) - (g \circ f)(x)}{h} = g'[f(x)]f'(x)$$
$$+ \{g'[f(x)]\psi(h) + \varphi[f(x+h) - f(x)][f'(x) + \psi(h)]\},$$

and the result follows since $f(x+h) - f(x) = o(1)$.

If, on the other hand, $f(x + h_n) = f(x)$ for $h_n \neq 0$, $\lim_n h_n = 0$, then $f'(x) = 0$, and $(g \circ f)(x + h_n) = (g \circ f)(x)$, $n = 1, 2, \cdots$, so that $(g \circ f)'(x) = 0$, if it exists. That it exists follows since, in this case, if $f(x+h) \neq f(x)$, we have $[(g \circ f)(x+h) - (g \circ f)(x)]/h = \{g'[f(x] + \varphi[f(x+h) - f(x)]\}\psi(h)$.

Example B We apply this fact to find the derivative of $\log_e |x|$, $x \neq 0$.

Let L be the function given by $\log_e |x|$. Consider the function f given by e^x. Then,

$$x = (L \circ f)(x), \quad \text{for every } x.$$

By the chain rule,

$$1 = L'[f(x)]e^x,$$

so that

$$L'[f(x)] = \frac{1}{f(x)}.$$

Since $f(x)$ assumes all positive values, for $x > 0$, this yields

$$(\log_e x)' = \frac{1}{x}.$$

It is then easy to see that

$$(\log_e |\mathbf{x}|)' = \frac{1}{x}, \qquad x \neq 0.$$

3. PROPERTIES OF DERIVATIVES

We shall see in the next chapter that, for every continuous f, there is a g such that $f = g'$. In other words, every continuous function is a derivative. At this time, we point out that there are derivatives which are not continuous.

For example, let $f: R \to R$ be the function

$$f(x) = \begin{cases} x^2 \sin \dfrac{1}{x}, & x \neq 0 \\ 0, & x = 0. \end{cases}$$

The reader can easily verify that f' exists everywhere, and

$$f'(x) = \begin{cases} 2x \sin 1/x - \cos 1/x, & x \neq 0 \\ 0, & x = 0. \end{cases}$$

Thus f' exists everywhere but, as is easily verified, is not continuous at $x = 0$.

We now state two properties of derivatives which indicate that they do retain some of the flavor of continuity. The first of these asserts the following:

If f is the derivative of a function g, then f is the limit of a sequence of continuous functions.

Proof

Since g is differentiable, it is continuous. The functions g_n, $n = 1, 2, \cdots$, defined by $g_n(x) = g(x + 1/n)$ are also continuous, as are the functions $n(g_n - g)$. Since f is the derivative of g, it follows that

$$f = \lim_n n(g_n - g),$$

so that f is the limit of a sequence of continuous functions. ∎

If I is an open interval, $f\colon I \to \mathrm{R}$ is said to have the **Darboux,** or intermediate value, property on I if, for every $a, b \in I$, for every η between $f(a)$ and $f(b)$, there is a ξ between a and b such that $f(\xi) = \eta$. We have shown that every continuous function has the Darboux property. Although derivatives need not be continuous, they have the Darboux property.

Theorem 1

If I is an open interval, and $f\colon I \to R$ is a derivative, then f has the Darboux property.

Proof

It suffices to let $a, b \in I$, $a < b$, to suppose that $f(a) < 0 < f(b)$, and to show that there is a $\xi \in (a, b)$ such that $f(\xi) = 0$.

There is a function g such that $g' = f$. The function g is continuous, so that it has a minimum value on $[a, b]$. Since $g'(a) < 0$, there is an $h > 0$ such that $a + h < b$ and $g(a + h) < g(a)$. Since $g'(b) > 0$, there is an $h' > 0$ such that $b - h' > a$ and $g(b - h') < g(b)$. The minimum value of g on $[a, b]$ is thus attained at some $\xi \in (a, b)$. We show that $g'(\xi) = 0$. Since for all $x < \xi$, $[g(\xi) - g(x)]/(\xi - x) \leq 0$, it follows that $g'(\xi) \leq 0$. Since for all $x > \xi$, $[g(\xi) - g(x)]/(\xi - x) \geq 0$, it follows that $g'(\xi) \geq 0$. Thus, $f(\xi) = g'(\xi) = 0$. ∎

A related property is called **Rolle's theorem.**

Theorem 2

If $I = [a, b]$ is a closed interval, $f: I \to \mathrm{R}$ is continuous on I, differentiable on (a, b), and $f(a) = f(b)$, there is a $\xi \in (a, b)$ such that $f'(\xi) = 0$.

Proof

If f is constant on I, the result is obvious. Suppose f is not constant. Then either its maximum or minimum is attained at some $\xi \in (a, b)$. It follows, as in the proof of Theorem 1, that $f'(\xi) = 0$. ∎

Rolle's theorem has important consequences. One of these is the *mean value theorem* which we state as

Corollary 1

If $I = [a, b]$ is a closed interval, and $f: I \to \mathrm{R}$ is continuous on I and differentiable on (a, b), there is a $\xi \in (a, b)$ such that

$$f(b) - f(a) = f'(\xi)(b - a).$$

Proof

Define an auxiliary function F by

$$F(x) = [f(b) - f(a)](x - a) - (b - a)[f(x) - f(a)].$$

The function F is continuous on $[a, b]$, differentiable on (a, b), and $F(a) = F(b) = 0$. By Rolle's theorem, there is a $\xi \in (a, b)$ with $F'(\xi) = 0$. Thus

$$f(b) - f(a) - (b - a)f'(\xi) = 0. \quad ∎$$

4. TAYLOR'S THEOREM

Suppose $f: I \to \mathrm{R}$ is differentiable. Then $f': I \to \mathrm{R}$. If f' is differentiable, then its derivative is called the second derivative of f. In this case, f is said to be twice differentiable. It is clear that a function may be n times differentiable for any natural number n.

The notation

$$f, f', f^{(2)}, \cdots, f^{(n)}, \cdots$$

will be used for the function and its derivatives.

If $f^{(n)}$ exists and is continuous, then f is said to be **of class** C^n. If f is of class C^n, it is clear that it is of class C^j for every $j < n$. It is easy to find examples of functions which are of class C^n, but not of class C^{n+1}, for every n. For example, the function f given by

$$f(x) = \begin{cases} x^{n+1}, & x \geq 0 \\ 0, & x < 0 \end{cases}$$

has this property.

If all the derivatives of f exist, f is said to be **of class C^∞**. If f is of class C^∞ then all its derivatives are continuous.

If a function f is $n + 1$ times differentiable, then it may be approximated, in a neighborhood of a point, by a polynomial of degree n. The error is given in terms of the $(n + 1)$st derivative. This is the substance of Taylor's formula.

Theorem 3

If f is $n + 1$ times differentiable on an interval containing points a, b then

$$f(b) = f(a) + (b - a)f'(a) + \cdots + \frac{(b - a)^n}{n!} f^{(n)}(a) + \frac{(b - a)^{n+1}}{(n + 1)!} f^{n+1}(\xi),$$

where ξ is some point between a and b.

Proof

We consider an appropriate auxiliary function F and apply Rolle's theorem. Let

$$F(x) = f(b) - \left\{ f(x) + (b - x)f'(x) + \cdots + \frac{(b - x)^n}{n!} f^{(n)}(x) \right\} + c(b - x)^{n+1},$$

where c will be specified in a moment. Now, F is continuous and differentiable on $[a, b]$ and $F(b) = 0$. If we choose

$$c = \frac{1}{(b - a)^{n+1}} \times \left\{ -f(b) + f(a) + (b - a)f'(a) + \cdots + \frac{(b - a)^n}{n!} f^{(n)}(a) \right\}$$

then $F(a) = 0$.

By Rolle's theorem, there is a $\xi \in (a, b)$ such that $F'(\xi) = 0$. Then

$$0 = -f'(\xi) + f'(\xi) - \cdots + \frac{(b - \xi)^n}{n!} f^{(n+1)}(\xi) - c(n + 1)(b - \xi)^n.$$

It follows that

$$c = \frac{1}{(n+1)!} f^{(n+1)}(\xi).$$

We then obtain

$$f(b) = f(a) + (b-a)f'(a) + \cdots + \frac{(b-a)^n}{n!} f^{(n)}(a)$$
$$+ \frac{(b-a)^{n+1}}{(n+1)!} f^{(n+1)}(\xi),$$

for some ξ between a and b. ∎

Suppose $b = x$ and $a = 0$. We then obtain

$$f(x) = f(0) + xf'(0) + \cdots + \frac{x^n}{n!} f^{(n)}(0) + \frac{x^{n+1}}{(n+1)!} f^{n+1}(\xi),$$

where ξ is between 0 and x.

Example A Let $f(x) = \sin x$. Then

$$f'(x) = \cos x, \quad f^{(2)}(x) = -\sin x, \cdots.$$

We obtain

$$\sin x = x - \frac{x^3}{3!} + \frac{x^5}{5!} - \frac{x^6}{6!} \sin \xi$$

where ξ is between 0 and x.

Then

$\sin 0.5 = 0.47943$ with an error of no more than 0.00002.

5. INFINITELY DIFFERENTIABLE FUNCTIONS

Taylor's formula allows us to express a large variety of infinitely differentiable functions as infinite series of powers of $x - a$, where a is real.

Thus, if f is infinitely differentiable in an interval containing a, then for every n,

$$f(x) = f(a) + (x-a)f'(a) + \cdots + \frac{(x-a)^n}{n!} f^{(n)}(a)$$
$$+ \frac{(x-a)^{n+1}}{(n+1)!} f^{n+1}(\xi_n),$$

where, for every x, ξ_n is a number between a and x.

It is natural to associate the infinite series

$$f(a) + \sum_{n=1}^{\infty} \frac{(x-a)^n}{n!} f^{(n)}(a)$$

with the function f. This series is called the **Taylor series** of f.

Clearly, the Taylor series of f converges to $f(x)$ for those values of x for which

$$\lim_n \frac{(x-a)^{n+1}}{(n+1)!} f^{(n+1)}(\xi_n) = 0.$$

Example A Let $f(x) = e^x$ and $a = 0$. The Taylor series of e^x is then

$$1 + x + \frac{x^2}{2!} + \cdots + \frac{x^n}{n!} + \cdots.$$

The Taylor formula is

$$1 + x + \frac{x^2}{2!} + \cdots + \frac{x^n}{n!} + \frac{x^{n+1}}{(n+1)!} e^{\xi_n}, \qquad 0 < \xi_n < x.$$

Now, $\lim_n \frac{x^{n+1}}{(n+1)!} e^{\xi_n} = 0$, so that the series converges to the function, for all x.

Example B Let $f(x) = \sin x$. The Taylor series, with $a = 0$, in this case is

$$x - \frac{x^3}{3!} + \frac{x^5}{5!} + \cdots + (-1)^n \frac{x^{2n+1}}{(2n+1)!} + \cdots.$$

We leave it to the reader to verify that the series converges to $\sin x$ for all x.

Example C Let $f(x) = \log x$, $x > 0$. The Taylor series, with $a = 1$ in this case, is

$$(x-1) - \frac{(x-1)^2}{2} + \frac{(x-1)^3}{3} + \cdots + (-1)^{n+1} \frac{(x-1)^n}{n} + \cdots$$

We leave it to the reader to verify that the series converges to $\log x$ for all x for which $|x - 1| < 1$.

Example D We now consider an example of an infinitely differentiable function f whose Taylor series converges, but not to f.

Let

$$f(x) = \begin{cases} e^{-1/x^2}, & x \neq 0 \\ 0, & x = 0. \end{cases}$$

We leave it to the reader to show that if p is any polynomial, then

$$\lim_{x \to 0} p(1/x)e^{-1/x^2} = 0.$$

(Hint: $e^x > x^n/n!$ for every $x > 0$.)

From this fact, it follows easily that f is infinitely differentiable and that $f^{(n)}(0) = 0$, $n = 1, 2, \cdots$. The Taylor series of f, with $a = 0$, thus converges to the zero function, not to f.

Chapter 9 will be devoted entirely to a study of series of the form $\sum_{n=0}^{\infty} a_n x^n$. Such series are called power series.

EXERCISES

1.1 Give an example of a continuous function which is not differentiable on a dense set.

2.1 If f and g are n times differentiable, obtain a formula for the nth derivative of fg.

2.2 If f is differentiable and not 0, show that

$$\left(\frac{1}{f}\right)' = -\frac{f'}{f^2}.$$

2.3 If f and g are infinitely differentiable, show that $f \circ g$ is infinitely differentiable.

2.4 If $x = \cos^3 t$ and $y = t \sin^3 t$, find

$$\frac{d^2y}{dx^2}.$$

3.1 Verify that the derivative of

$$f(x) = \begin{cases} x^2 \sin 1/x, & x \neq 0 \\ 0, & x = 0 \end{cases}$$

is

$$f'(x) = \begin{cases} 2x \sin 1/x - \cos 1/x, & x \neq 0 \\ 0, & x = 0. \end{cases}$$

3.2 The right derivative of f exists at x_0 and is equal to k if, for every $\epsilon > 0$, there is a $\delta > 0$ such that $0 < x - x_0 < \delta$ implies that $|[f(x) - f(x_0)]/(x - x_0) - k| < \epsilon$. The left derivative is defined similarly. Show that the set of points where the left and right derivatives both exist, but are not equal, is countable.

3.3 If $\lim_{h \to 0} [f(x + h) + f(x - h) - 2f(x)]/h^2$ exists, then f is said to have a generalized second derivative at x which is given by the above limit. Show that if f has a generalized second derivative at x, then it has a second derivative at x, and the two are equal.

3.4 Give an example of a function which does not have a second derivative at a point but does have a generalized second derivative there.

3.5 If f is twice differentiable, and the second derivative is never negative, show that f is convex.

3.6 Give an example of a convex function whose derivative does not exist on a dense set.

3.7 If f is convex, show that its right and left derivatives exist everywhere and are nondecreasing.

3.8 Given an arbitrary countable set S, give an example of a convex function whose derivative does not exist at any point in S but does exist at every point not in S.

3.9 If a function is continuous on $[a, b]$, and its generalized second derivative is zero everywhere on $[a, b]$, show that the function is linear on $[a, b]$.

3.10 Prove the generalized mean value theorem which says that if f and g are continuous on $[a, b]$, and differentiable on (a, b), there is a $\xi \in (a, b)$ such that

$$f'(\xi)[g(b) - g(a)] = g'(\xi)[f(b) - f(a)].$$

4.1 Give an example of a series of continuously differentiable functions which converges uniformly but whose derivatives do not converge.

4.2 Find log 1.3 to 4 decimals, and prove your answer correct.

4.3 Find $\sqrt[3]{7}$ to 6 decimals, and prove your answer correct.

5.1 Show that if p is any polynomial, then

$$\lim_{x \to 0} p(1/x)e^{-1/x^2} = 0.$$

5.2 Show that the function

$$f(x) = \begin{cases} e^{-1/x^2}, & x \neq 0 \\ 0, & x = 0 \end{cases}$$

is infinitely differentiable.

5.3 If (a, b) is an open interval, give an example of an infinitely differentiable function which is positive on (a, b) and zero everywhere else.

5.4 For every continuous function f on the reals, show that there is a sequence of infinitely differentiable functions which converges uniformly to f.

5.5 Give an example of a function which has the Darboux property, but has at most one point of continuity.

5.6 If $f: [a, b] \to [c, d]$ is bijective, differentiable, with continuous derivative which is always positive, then the inverse function has the same property.

CHAPTER 8

INTEGRATION

1. DEFINITION OF INTEGRAL

We associate, with every bounded function f on a closed interval $I = [a, b]$, two numbers called the upper and lower integrals of f on I. The lower integral is not greater than the upper integral for any given function f and, if the two are equal, the function is said to be integrable on $[a, b]$ in the sense of Riemann.

Before giving the definitions, we must introduce some auxiliary notions. For any interval J, we designate the length of J by $|J|$.

By a **partition** π of the closed interval I we mean a finite ordered set

$$\pi = \{a = x_0 < x_1 < \cdots < x_n = b\}.$$

The closed intervals

$$I_j = [x_{j-1}, x_j], \qquad j = 1, \cdots, n,$$

are called the **intervals** of the partition. The **norm,** $\|\pi\|$, of the partition is

$$\|\pi\| = \max [\, |I_j| : j = 1, \cdots, n].$$

For every partition $\pi = \{a = x_0 < x_1 < \cdots < x_n = b\}$, let

$$u(f, \pi) = \sum_{j=1}^{n} \sup [f(x): x \in I_j] \cdot |I_j|$$

and

$$l(f, \pi) = \sum_{j=1}^{n} \inf [f(x): x \in I_j] \cdot |I_j|,$$

where f is a bounded function defined on I.

The definition implies that

$$l(f, \pi) \leq u(f, \pi).$$

If $\pi = \{a = x_0 < x_1 < \cdots < x_n = b\}$ and $\pi' = \{a = y_0 < y_1 < \cdots < y_m = b\}$ are partitions of I, π is called a **refinement** of π' if π' is a subset of π.

We show that if π is a refinement of π' then

$$u(f, \pi) \leq u(f, \pi') \quad \text{and} \quad l(f, \pi) \geq l(f, \pi').$$

Let $I_1, \cdots, I_n$ be the intervals of π and $J_1, \cdots, J_m$ the intervals of π'. For every, $i = 1, \cdots, m$, let $I_{i1}, \cdots, I_{in_i}$ be those among the intervals $I_1, \cdots, I_n$ which are contained in J_i. Then

$$\begin{aligned} u(f, \pi) &= \sum_{j=1}^{n} \sup [f(x): x \in I_j] \cdot |I_j| \\ &= \sum_{i=1}^{m} \sum_{r=1}^{n_i} \sup [f(x): x \in I_{ir}] \cdot |I_{ir}| \\ &\leq \sum_{i=1}^{m} \sup [f(x): x \in J_i] \cdot |J_i| \\ &= u(f, \pi'). \end{aligned}$$

The proof that $l(f, \pi) \geq l(f, \pi')$ is similar.

We have shown that

(a) For every partition π,

$$l(f, \pi) \leq u(f, \pi).$$

(b) If π and π' are partitions, with π a refinement of π', then

$$u(f, \pi) \leq u(f, \pi')$$

and

$$l(f, \pi) \geq l(f, \pi').$$

From **(a)** and **(b)**, we obtain the more interesting

(c) If π_1 and π_2 are any partitions, then

$$l(f, \pi_1) \leq u(f, \pi_2).$$

Proof

Let π be a partition which is a refinement of both π_1 and π_2. Then

$$l(f, \pi_1) \leq l(f, \pi) \leq u(f, \pi) \leq u(f, \pi_2). \quad \blacksquare$$

We now define the **upper** and **lower integrals,** $\overline{\int} f$ and $\underline{\int} f$, of f on $[a, b]$ as

$$\overline{\int} f = \inf u(f, \pi), \qquad \underline{\int} f = \sup l(f, \pi),$$

where the supremum and infimum are taken over all partitions π of $[a, b]$.

By **(c)**, we have

(d) For every bounded f on a closed interval $[a, b]$, we have

$$\overline{\int} f \geq \underline{\int} f.$$

If $\overline{\int} f = \underline{\int} f$, we say that f is **Riemann integrable,** and write $\int f$ for their common value. We also write

$$\int_a^b f, \quad \text{or} \quad \int_a^b f(x)\, dx,$$

for the integral.

Example Let $f(x) = x^2$ on $[0, t]$, $t > 0$. Consider the partition π_n obtained by dividing $[0, t]$ into n equal parts. Then

$$u(f, \pi_n) = \frac{t^3}{n^3}(1^2 + 2^2 + \cdots + n^2) = \frac{t^3}{n^3}\frac{n(2n+1)(n+1)}{6}$$
$$= \frac{t^3}{6}\left(2 + \frac{1}{n}\right)\left(1 + \frac{1}{n}\right),$$

and

$$l(f, \pi_n) = \frac{t^3}{n^3}(1^2 + 2^2 + \cdots + (n-1)^2) = \frac{t^3}{n^3}\frac{n(2n-1)(n-1)}{6}$$
$$= \frac{t^3}{6}\left(2 - \frac{1}{n}\right)\left(1 - \frac{1}{n}\right).$$

It follows that $\overline{\int} f \leq \frac{t^3}{3}$ and $\underline{\int} f \geq \frac{t^3}{3}$. Hence, f is integrable on $[0, t]$, and $\int_0^t x^2\, dx = \frac{t^3}{3}$.

The following statement regarding the existence of the integral is obvious.

A bounded function f, on a closed interval $[a, b]$, is integrable if and only if, for every $\epsilon > 0$ there is a partition π such that

$$u(f, \pi) < l(f, \pi) + \epsilon.$$

2. CRITERIA FOR EXISTENCE OF INTEGRALS

Our first criterion depends upon the following simple fact.

If I is a closed interval, and π is a partition of I, then for every $\epsilon > 0$, there is a $\delta > 0$, such that for any partition π' of I, whose norm is less than δ, the sum of the lengths of those intervals of π', which are not contained in intervals of π, is less than ϵ.

Proof

If k is the number of intervals in the partition π, we need only take $\delta = \epsilon/(2k)$.

Theorem 1

If a bounded function f, on a closed interval $I = [a, b]$ is integrable then, for every $\epsilon > 0$, there is a $\delta > 0$, such that if $\pi = \{a = x_0 < x_1 < \cdots < x_m = b\}$ is any partition of norm less than δ, and $\xi_j \in I_j$, $j = 1, \cdots, m$, then

$$\left| \int f - \sum_{j=1}^{m} f(\xi_j)\, |I_j| \right| < \epsilon.$$

Proof

Let $M = \sup [\, |f(x)| : x \in I]$, and let π' be a partition of I for which $u(f, \pi') - l(f, \pi') < \epsilon/2$.

Let $\delta > 0$ be the δ of the above remark which corresponds to π' and $\dfrac{\epsilon}{2M}$. Now, let π be any partition of I of norm less than δ. Let $I_1, \cdots, I_k$ be the intervals of π which are contained in intervals of the partition π', and let $I_{k+1}, \cdots, I_m$ be the remaining intervals of the partition π. Then

$$\sum_{j=k+1}^{m} |I_j| < \frac{\epsilon}{2M}. \text{ Let } \xi_j \in I_j, j = 1, \cdots, m.$$

Then

$$\sum_{j=1}^{m} f(\xi_j)\, |I_j| = \sum_{j=1}^{k} f(\xi_j)\, |I_j| + \sum_{j=k+1}^{m} f(\xi_j)\, |I_j|$$

$$< u(f, \pi') + M \cdot \frac{\epsilon}{2M} = u(f, \pi') + \frac{\epsilon}{2}.$$

In similar fashion,

$$\sum_{j=1}^{m} f(\xi_j)\, |I_j| > l(f, \pi) - \frac{\epsilon}{2}.$$

It follows that

$$\int f - \epsilon \le \sum_{j=1}^{m} f(\xi_j)\, |I_j| \le \int f + \epsilon. \quad \blacksquare$$

A converse to this theorem holds, but we leave its formulation and proof to the reader.

A set S will be said to have **content zero** if, for every $\epsilon > 0$, it can be covered by a finite set of intervals, the sum of whose lengths is less than ϵ.

Theorem 2

If $I = [a, b]$ is a closed interval, and $f\colon I \to \mathrm{R}$ is bounded, then f is Riemann integrable if and only if, for every $k > 0$, the set of points at which the saltus of f is greater than or equal to k has content zero.

Proof

Suppose the condition holds. Let $\epsilon > 0$ and let

$$E_\epsilon = [x\colon w(x) \geq \epsilon].$$

Let $M = \sup\,[|f(x)|\colon x \in I]$. Now, E_ϵ may be covered by disjoint closed intervals $I_1, \cdots, I_r$, the sum of whose lengths is less than $\epsilon/(2M)$. Let π be a partition of I, the intervals of which are $I_1, \cdots, I_r$, together with intervals $I_{r+1}, \cdots, I_m$, in each of which the saltus of f is less than ϵ. Then,

$$u(f, \pi) - l(f, \pi) < \epsilon\,|I| + 2M \cdot \frac{\epsilon}{2M} = \epsilon(|I| + 1).$$

It follows that f is integrable.

For the converse, suppose there is a $k > 0$ such that the set

$$E_k = [x\colon w(x) \geq k]$$

cannot be covered by a finite set of intervals the sum of whose lengths is less than k. Then, for every partition π of I, it follows readily that

$$u(f, \pi) - l(f, \pi) \geq k^2.$$

Accordingly, the function f is not integrable. ∎

For our next result, we need the fact that if S is compact and is the union of a countable number of sets, each of which is of content zero, then S has content zero.

Proof

Let $S = \bigcup_{n=1}^{\infty} S_n$, where S_n has content zero, $n = 1, 2, \cdots$. Let $\epsilon > 0$. Then S_n is covered by a finite set of open intervals, the sum of whose lengths is less than $\epsilon/2^n$. Then S is covered by a countable set of open intervals, the sum of whose lengths is less than ϵ. But, by the Borel covering theorem, a finite number of these intervals covers S. It follows that S has content zero. ∎

Theorem 3

A bounded function f on a closed interval I is Riemann integrable if and only if its set of points of discontinuity is the union of a countable number of sets each of content zero.

Proof

Suppose f is Riemann integrable. Then, for every n, the set D_n of points at which the saltus of f is not less than $1/n$ has content zero. But $D = \bigcup_{n=1}^{\infty} D_n$, where D is the set of points of discontinuity of f.

Suppose, conversely, the set of points of discontinuity of f is the union of a countable number of sets of content zero. Then, for every $k > 0$, the set

$$E_k = [x: w(x) \geq k]$$

is a compact set with the same property. By the above remark, E_k has content zero. It follows that f is Riemann integrable.

3. THE CLASS OF INTEGRABLE FUNCTIONS

All functions considered are bounded and defined on a closed interval.

We first note that if S and T have content zero then $S \cup T$ has content zero.

This fact, together with Theorem 3 of the last section, and facts about continuous functions taken from Chapter 4, allows us to make the following statements whose proofs are now easy and may be left to the reader.

(a) If f and g are Riemann integrable, then $f + g$ is Riemann integrable.

(b) If f and g are Riemann integrable, then fg is Riemann integrable.

(c) If f is Riemann integrable and a is a real number, then af is Riemann integrable.

(d) If f is Riemann integrable, then $|f|$ is Riemann integrable.

(e) If f and g are Riemann integrable, then $\max(f, g)$ and $\min(f, g)$ are Riemann integrable.

(f) If f is Riemann integrable, and $1/f$ is bounded, then $1/f$ is Riemann integrable.

(g) If I and J are closed intervals, $J \subset I$, and f is Riemann integrable on I, then f is Riemann integrable on J.

(h) If f is Riemann integrable on I and J and $K \subset I \cup J$, then f is Riemann integrable on K.

We proceed to some quantitative facts.

(a) If $I = [a, b]$ is a closed interval, f is Riemann integrable on I, and $c \in (a, b)$, then

$$\int_a^b f = \int_a^c f + \int_c^b f.$$

Proof

The function f is integrable on $[a, c]$ and on $[c, b]$. Let $\epsilon > 0$. There are partitions π_1 of $[a, c]$ and π_2 of $[c, b]$ such that

$$l(f, \pi_1) \geq u(f, \pi_1) - \frac{\epsilon}{2} \quad \text{and} \quad l(f, \pi_2) \geq u(f, \pi_2) - \frac{\epsilon}{2}.$$

Let π be the partition of $[a, b]$ obtained by adjoining the intervals of the partition π_1 to those of the partition π_2. Then

$$l(f, \pi_1) + l(f, \pi_2) = l(f, \pi)$$

and

$$u(f, \pi_1) + u(f, \pi_2) = u(f, \pi).$$

Then,

$$l(f, \pi) \leq \int_a^c f + \int_c^b f \leq l(f, \pi) + \epsilon$$

and

$$l(f, \pi) \leq \int_a^b f \leq l(f, \pi) + \epsilon.$$

Since this holds for every $\epsilon > 0$,

$$\int_a^c f + \int_c^b f = \int_a^b f. \quad \blacksquare$$

(b) If f and g are Riemann integrable on a closed interval $I = [a, b]$, then

$$\int (f+g) = \int f + \int g.$$

Proof

For every partition π of $[a, b]$,

$$l(f+g, \pi) \geq l(f, \pi) + l(g, \pi)$$

and

$$u(f+g, \pi) \leq u(f, \pi) + u(g, \pi).$$

Let $\epsilon > 0$ and let π be such that $l(f, \pi) > u(f, \pi) - \epsilon/2$ and $l(g, \pi) > u(g, \pi) - \epsilon/2$. Then

$$\begin{aligned} l(f, \pi) + l(g, \pi) &\leq l(f+g, \pi) \\ &\leq \int (f+g) \leq u(f+g, \pi) \\ &\leq u(f, \pi) + u(g, \pi) \\ &< l(f, \pi) + l(g, \pi) + \epsilon. \end{aligned}$$

Since

$$l(f, \pi) + l(g, \pi) \leq \int f + \int g < l(f, \pi) + l(g, \pi) + \epsilon,$$

it follows that $\int f + \int g = \int (f+g)$. ∎

We introduce an orientation for intervals, so that $[b, a] = -[a, b]$. Then

$$\int_b^a f = -\int_a^b f.$$

The next few statements are easy, and the proofs are left to the reader.

(c) If f is integrable on $[a, b]$ and a is real, then

$$\int af = a \int f.$$

(d) If f is integrable on $[a, b]$, then

$$\int |f| \geq \left| \int f \right|.$$

(e) If $f(x) \geq g(x)$, for every $x \in [a, b]$, and both functions are bounded, then $\bar{\int} f \geq \bar{\int} g$ and $\underline{\int} f \geq \underline{\int} g$.

As a corollary to this simple fact, if f is integrable on $[a, b]$ and

$$m \leq f(x) \leq M$$

for all $x \in [a, b]$, then

$$m(b - a) \leq \int f \leq M(b - a).$$

4. INTEGRALS OF LIMITS

Let I be a closed interval. It is possible for a sequence $\{f_n\}$ of integrable functions on I to converge to a function f which is not integrable. Or, it is possible for $\{f_n\}$ to converge to a function f which is integrable, but for which

$$\lim_n \int f_n \neq \int f_n.$$

Example A Let $[a, b]$ be a closed interval, and let $\{r_n\}$ be the rationals in $[a, b]$. Let

$$f_n(x) = \begin{cases} 1 & , x = r_i, \ i = 1, \cdots, n \\ 0 & , \text{elsewhere.} \end{cases}$$

Then, for each $n = 1, 2, \cdots, f_n$ is integrable and $\int f_n = 0$.

Now,

$$\lim_n f_n = f,$$

where

$$f(x) = \begin{cases} 1 & , x \text{ rational} \\ 0 & , x \text{ irrational.} \end{cases}$$

It is clear that $\bar{\int} f = 1$ and $\underline{\int} f = 0$, so that f is not integrable.

Example B Let f_n: $[0, 1] \to R$ be defined by

$$f_n(x) = \begin{cases} n^2 x & , 0 \leq x \leq 1/n, \\ -n^2 x + 2n & , 1/n \leq x \leq 2/n, \\ 0 & , 2/n \leq x \leq 1. \end{cases}$$

Then, $\{f_n\}$ converges to f, the zero function. Now,

$$\int f_n = \frac{1}{2}(n)\left(\frac{2}{n}\right) = 1, \qquad \text{for every } n,$$

but $\int f = 0$.

In contrast with these examples, we have

Theorem 4

If $\{f_n\}$ is a sequence of Riemann integrable functions on $I = [a, b]$, which converges uniformly on I to f, then f is Riemann integrable and

$$\lim_n \int_a^b f_n = \int_a^b f.$$

Proof

Let $\epsilon > 0$. There is an N such that $n > N$ implies $|f(x) - f_n(x)| < \frac{\epsilon}{b - a}$, for every $x \in I$. Then

$$\overline{\int} f < \overline{\int} f_n + \epsilon = \int f_n + \epsilon$$

and

$$\underline{\int} f > \underline{\int} f_n - \epsilon = \int f_n - \epsilon.$$

The result follows easily.

5. THE FUNDAMENTAL THEOREM OF CALCULUS

The operations of integration and differentiation are inverses of each other, as we now show for the case where the function being integrated is continuous.

Let $f\colon [a, b] \to R$ be continuous. Let $F\colon [a, b] \to R$ be a function such that, for every $x, y \in [a, b]$,

$$F(x) - F(y) = \int_y^x f.$$

For $x \in (a, b)$ and $h \neq 0$ so that $x + h \in [a, b]$, we have

$$\frac{F(x + h) - F(x)}{h} = \frac{1}{h}\int_x^{x+h} f = f(\xi),$$

where $\xi \in [x, x + h]$, since

$$\min\{f(t)\colon t \in [x, x + h]\} \leq \frac{1}{h}\int_x^{x+h} f \leq \max\{f(t)\colon t \in [x, x + h]\},$$

and f has the Darboux property.

It follows from the continuity of f that

$$F'(x) = \lim_{h \to 0} \frac{F(x+h) - F(x)}{h} = f(x).$$

At the end points, this argument shows that f is the one sided derivative of F.

We have proved

Theorem 5

If f is continuous on an open interval (a, b) and there is an F such that for every $x, y \in (a, b)$,

$$F(y) - F(x) = \int_x^y f(t)\, dt$$

then F is differentiable and $F' = f$.

If $[a, b]$ is closed then f is the one-sided derivative of F at the end points.

Corollary

Every continuous function is a derivative.

Proof

Let f be continuous on an open interval (a, b). Fix $x_0 \in (a, b)$. Let

$$F(x) = \int_{x_0}^x f(t)\, dt,$$

for every $x \in (a, b)$. Then for every $x, y \in (a, b)$,

$$F(x) - F(y) = \int_y^x f(t)\, dt.$$

By the theorem, $f = F'$ on (a, b). ▮

Theorem 6

If $f \in C^1$ on an open interval (c, d) and $[a, b] \subset (c, d)$ then

$$\int_a^b f' = f(b) - f(a).$$

Proof

Let $\pi = \{a = x_0 < x_1 < \cdots < x_n = b\}$ be a partition of $[a, b]$. By the mean value theorem, there is $\xi_i \in [x_{i-1}, x_i]$, $i = 1, \cdots, n$ with

$$f'(\xi_i)(x_i - x_{i-1}) = f(x_i) - f(x_{i-1}),$$

so that

$$\sum_{i=1}^{n} f'(\xi_i)(x_i - x_{i-1}) = \sum_{i=1}^{n} [f(x_i) - f(x_{i-1})]$$
$$= f(b) - f(a).$$

The theorem follows from the Riemann integrability of f'. ∎

As an application, we prove

Theorem 7

Let J be an open interval, and $\{f_n\}$ a sequence of functions of class C^1, i.e., each f_n has a continuous derivative on J. Then, if $\sum_{n=1}^{\infty} f_n$ converges uniformly to f and $\sum_{n=1}^{\infty} f_n'$ converges uniformly to g, on every closed subinterval $I \subset J$, then f is differentiable and $f' = g$.

Proof

Let $[a, b] = I \subset J$. For every n, let

$$s_n = \sum_{k=1}^{n} f_k.$$

Then

$$s_n' = \sum_{k=1}^{n} f_k'.$$

Now,

$$\int_a^b s_n' = s_n(b) - s_n(a).$$

Since $\{s_n'\}$ converges uniformly to g,

$$\lim_n \int_a^b s_n' = \int_a^b g.$$

Moreover,

$$\lim_n \{s_n(b) - s_n(a)\} = f(b) - f(a).$$

Hence, for every $[a, b] \subset J$,

$$f(b) - f(a) = \int_a^b g.$$

It follows that $g = f'$ on J. ∎

We prove the following slight extension of the fundamental theorem of the calculus.

If $[a, b]$ is a closed interval, f is continuous on $[a, b]$, and f' exists and is bounded and continuous on (a, b), then

$$\int_a^b f' = f(b) - f(a).$$

Proof

On every closed interval $[c, d] \subset (a, b)$,

$$\int_c^d f' = f(d) - f(c),$$

and the result follows by taking limits. The limit of the right side exists because f is continuous. The limit of the left side exists because it is equal to the right side. ∎

Suppose, now, that $[a, b]$ is a closed interval, that f is continuous on $[a, b]$, and that f' exists and is bounded and continuous on (a, b), except at a finite set of points. Then

$$\int_a^b f' = f(b) - f(a).$$

The proof of this more general statement may now be left to the reader. It has an important application.

Integration by parts If f and g are continuous on $[a, b]$ and are differentiable, except at a finite number of points in (a, b) with bounded and continuous derivatives, then

$$\int_a^b fg' = f(b)g(b) - f(a)g(a) - \int_a^b f'g.$$

Proof

We may apply the fundamental theorem of the calculus to the function fg to obtain

$$\int_a^b (fg)' = f(b)g(b) - f(a)g(a).$$

But,

$$(fg)' = fg' + f'g. \quad ∎$$

We shall also prove a change of variables formula.

Change of Variable Theorem Let f be Riemann integrable on $[a, b]$ and let

$$g\colon [c, d] \to [a, b]$$

be bijective and differentiable, with positive continuous derivative. Then

$$\int_a^b f = \int_c^d (f \circ g) \cdot g'.$$

Proof

We first note that, since (see Exercise 2.6) the image of a set of content zero under g also has content zero, the function $(f \circ g) \cdot g'$ is Riemann integrable.

Let $\pi = [c = x_0 < x_1 < \cdots < x_n = d]$ be a partition of $[c, d]$. Then

$$\pi' = [a = g(x_0) < g(x_1) < \cdots < g(x_n) = b]$$

is a partition of $[a, b]$.

For each $i = 1, \cdots, n$, there is a $\xi_i \in [x_{i-1}, x_i]$ such that

$$g'(\xi_i)(x_i - x_{i-1}) = g(x_i) - g(x_{i-1}).$$

Then,

$$\sum_{i=1}^{n} g'(\xi_i) f[g(\xi_i)](x_i - x_{i-1}) = \sum_{i=1}^{n} f[g(\xi_i)][g(x_i) - g(x_{i-1})].$$

As the norm of π converges to zero, so does the norm of π', and we obtain

$$\int_c^d (f \circ g) \cdot g' = \int_a^b f. \quad \blacksquare$$

6. INTEGRAL ON AN OPEN INTERVAL

Let $I = (a, b)$ be an open interval, finite or infinite in length. Let $f: I \to \mathrm{R}$ have the property that it is Riemann integrable on every closed subinterval of I. We define the integral of f on I in terms of the integrals of f on the closed subintervals of I.

We do this first for the case where the function f is nonnegative, and the interval I is finite. Then, we define the integral of f on I as

$$\lim_{\epsilon \to 0} \int_{a+\epsilon}^{b-\epsilon} f.$$

We say that f is *summable* on I if

$$\lim_{\epsilon \to 0} \int_{a+\epsilon}^{b-\epsilon} f < \infty.$$

If

$$\lim_{\epsilon \to 0} \int_{a+\epsilon}^{b-\epsilon} f = \infty,$$

we say that f is nonsummable on I.

Suppose now that f is defined on $(-\infty, \infty)$, is nonnegative, and is Riemann integrable on every closed interval $[a, b]$. We define the integral of f on $(-\infty, \infty)$ as

$$\lim_{n\to\infty} \int_{-n}^{n} f.$$

If $\lim_{n\to\infty} \int_{-n}^{n} f < \infty$, we say that f is **summable.** Otherwise, we say f is nonsummable.

Now, let f be a function which is not necessarily nonnegative on I, finite or infinite, but which is Riemann integrable on every closed subinterval of I. We associate with f the two nonnegative functions f^+ and f^- defined by

$$f^+(x) = \max\,[f(x), 0]$$

and

$$f^-(x) = -\min\,[f(x), 0],$$

for every $x \in I$.

Then,

$$f = f^+ - f^-$$

and

$$|f| = f^+ + f^-.$$

We say that f is **summable** on I if both f^+ and f^- are summable, and define the integral of f as

$$\int f = \int f^+ - \int f^-.$$

If f^+ is not summable and f^- is summable, we define the integral of f as

$$\int f = \infty.$$

If f^+ is summable and f^- is not summable, we define the integral of f as

$$\int f = -\infty.$$

If neither f^+ nor f^- is summable, we do not talk about the integral of f at all.

Various properties of the integral, which were established for functions on a closed interval, hold for summable functions on an open interval. We relegate the development of these properties to the exercises.

We note, however, that if f^+ and f^- are both nonsummable, then we can obtain any value we please as

$$\lim_{\epsilon,\eta\to 0}\int_{a+\epsilon}^{b-\eta} f,$$

by properly choosing the manner in which ϵ and η converge to zero.

Example A Let $f(x) = \tan x$, $-\pi/2 < x < \pi/2$. Now,

$$\int_{-\pi/2+\eta}^{\pi/2-\epsilon} \tan x\,dx = \log\sec(\pi/2-\epsilon) - \log\sec(-\pi/2+\eta).$$

If we let $\epsilon = \eta$ and let ϵ converge to zero, the limit is zero. However, we can choose ϵ_n and η_n, $n = 1, 2, \cdots$, so that

$$\log\sec(\pi/2-\epsilon_n) - \log\sec(-\pi/2+\eta_n) = s_n,$$

where $\lim_n \epsilon_n = \lim_n \eta_n = 0$, and $\{s_n\}$ is any real sequence.

Example B Let $f(x) = x^{-1/2}$, $0 < x < 1$. Now,

$$\int_{\epsilon}^{1-\epsilon} x^{-1/2}\,dx = 2(\sqrt{1-\epsilon} - \sqrt{\epsilon}),$$

and it follows that

$$\int_0^1 x^{-1/2}\,dx = 2.$$

Example C Let $f(x) = e^{-x^2}$, $-\infty < x < \infty$. We note that

$$\int_{-\infty}^{\infty} e^{-x^2}\,dx < \infty,$$

if and only if $\sum_{n=1}^{\infty} e^{-n^2} < \infty$. But, $e^{-n^2} < \frac{1}{n^2}$, so that the function is summable.

7. FUNCTIONS OF BOUNDED VARIATION

We now consider an important generalization of the Riemann integral called the Riemann-Stieltjes integral.

For this purpose, we must discuss a special class of functions, the functions of bounded variation.

Let $I = [a, b]$, and let $f\colon I \to \mathrm{R}$. For every partition $\pi = \{a = x_0 < x_1 < \cdots < x_n = b\}$ of $[a, b]$, consider the number

$$v(f, \pi) = \sum_{i=1}^{n} |f(x_i) - f(x_{i-1})|.$$

If there is an M such that

$$v(f, \pi) \le M,$$

for all partitions π, then f is said to be of **bounded variation** on I. The number

$$V(f) = V(f; [a, b]) = \sup v(f, \pi),$$

where the supremum is taken for all partitions π, is then called the **variation** of f in the interval $[a, b]$.

Example The function f: $[-1, 1]$, defined by

$$f(x) = \begin{cases} x \sin 1/x, & x \neq 0 \\ 0, & x = 0 \end{cases}$$

is continuous, but is not of bounded variation.

We leave the proof of this to the reader.

We give some elementary properties of the variation of a function.

(a) For functions f and g defined on an interval $[a, b]$, $V(f + g; [a, b]) \le V(f; [a, b]) + V(g; [a, b])$.

(b) If f is defined on $[a, b]$, and a is real, then

$$V(af) = |a| \, V(f).$$

(c) If f is defined an $[a, b]$ and $c \in (a, b)$, then

$$V(f; [a, b]) = V(f; [a, c]) + V(f; [c, b]).$$

(d) If $\{f_n\}$ converges to f on $[a, b]$, then

$$\liminf_n V(f_n; [a, b]) \ge V(f; [a, b]).$$

We leave the proofs of **(a)**, **(b)**, and **(c)** to the reader. For **(d)**, suppose $V(f) = \infty$. Let $M > 0$. There is a partition $\pi = \{a = x_0 < x_1 < \cdots < x_n = b\}$ such that $v(f, \pi) > M + 1$. Let g be such that

$$|g(x_i) - f(x_i)| < \frac{1}{2n}, \qquad i = 0, 1, \cdots, n.$$

Then $v(g, \pi) > M$. It follows that, if $\{f_n\}$ converges to f, then $\lim_n V(f_n) = \infty$. Suppose $V(f) < \infty$. Let $\epsilon > 0$. There is a partition $\pi = \{a = x_0 < x_1 < \cdots < x_n = b\}$, such that $v(f, \pi) > V(f) - \epsilon/2$. Let g be such that

$$|g(x_i) - f(x_i)| < \frac{\epsilon}{4n}, \qquad i = 0, 1, \cdots, n.$$

Then $V(g) > V(f) - \epsilon$. It follows that if $\{f_n\}$ converges to f, then $\liminf_n V(f_n) \geq V(f)$.

(e) If f is continuous on $[a, b]$, then if $\{\pi_n\}$ is a sequence of partitions of $[a, b]$ whose norms converge to zero, we have

$$V(f) = \lim_n v(f, \pi_n).$$

Proof

Let $\epsilon > 0$, and let $\pi = \{a = x_0 < \cdots < x_n = b\}$ be a partition of $[a, b]$ such that $v(f, \pi) > V(f) - \epsilon/2$. There is a $\delta > 0$, such that $x, y \in [a, b]$, $|x - y| < \delta$ implies $|f(x) - f(y)| < \epsilon/(4n)$. It is easy to see that for every partition π' of $[a, b]$ of norm less than δ, $v(f, \pi') > v(f, \pi) - \epsilon/2$. Then $v(f, \pi') > V(f) - \epsilon$ and the result follows. ▮

(f) If $f: [a, b] \to R$ is continuous, then the curve defined by f has finite length if and only if f is of bounded variation.

Proof

For every partition π, it is immediate from the definitions that

$$v(f, \pi) \leq \lambda(f, \pi) \leq v(f, \pi) + (b - a),$$

so that

$$V(f) \leq L(f) \leq V(f) + (b - a),$$

and the result follows. ▮

(g) If $f: [a, b] \to R$ is of class C^1, and $[c, d] \subset (a, b)$, then f is of bounded variation on $[c, d]$ and

$$V(f) = \int_c^d |f'|.$$

Proof

Let $\pi = \{c = x_0 < \cdots < x_n = d\}$ be a partition of $[c, d]$. For every $i = 1, \cdots, n$, there is a $\xi_i \in [x_{i-1}, x_i]$ such that

$$|f(x_i) - f(x_{i-1})| = |f'(\xi_i)|\,[x_i - x_{i-1}].$$

Then,

$$v(f, \pi) = \sum_{i=1}^{n} |f'(\xi_i)|\,(x_i - x_{i-1}).$$

By choosing a sequence of partitions whose norms converge to zero, we obtain

$$V(f) = \int_c^d |f'|. \quad \blacksquare$$

8. STRUCTURE OF FUNCTIONS OF BOUNDED VARIATION

It is almost immediate from the definition that every monotonically nondecreasing function is of bounded variation. We now show that these are in a sense the only functions of bounded variation. Precisely, every function of bounded variation is the difference of two monotonically nondecreasing functions.

Let $I = [a, b]$ be a closed interval, and let

$$f: I \to \mathrm{R}$$

be of bounded variation on I.

For each $x \in [a, b]$, consider the variation $V(f; [a, x])$. The function g defined by

$$g(x) = V(f; [a, x])$$

is monotonically nondecreasing. We show that the function

$$h = g - f$$

is also monotonically nondecreasing.

Let $a \leq x < y \leq b$. Then

$$V(f; [x, y]) \geq |f(y) - f(x)|,$$

so that

$$\begin{aligned} h(y) - h(x) &= g(y) - f(y) - g(x) + f(x) \\ &= V(f; [a, y]) - V(f; [a, x]) - f(y) + f(x) \\ &= V(f; [x, y]) - [f(y) - f(x)] \geq 0. \end{aligned}$$

We have thus proved

Theorem 8

If f is of bounded variation on $[a, b]$, then

$$f = g - h,$$

where g and h are monotonically nondecreasing functions on $[a, b]$.

For the case where f is continuous, the functions g and h may be taken to be continuous. This follows from the fact that if f is continuous on $[a, b]$, and of bounded variation, then the function

$$g(x) = V(f; [a, x])$$

is continuous.

To prove this, let $\epsilon > 0$. There is a $\delta > 0$, such that $x, y \in [a, b]$ and $|x - y| < \delta$ implies $|f(x) - f(y)| < \epsilon$. Now, let $x \in [a, b]$ and let $\pi = \{a = x_0 < x_1 < \cdots < x_n = b\}$ be a partition such that $x_i = x$, $x_i - x_{i-1} < \delta$, $x_{i+1} - x_i < \delta$, for some $i = 1, \cdots, n$, and $v(f, \pi) \geq V(f; [a, b]) - \epsilon$.

It follows that

$$g(x_{i+1}) - g(x) = V(f; [x, x_{i+1}]) < 2\epsilon$$

and

$$g(x) - g(x_{i-1}) = V(f; [x_{i-1}, x]) < 2\epsilon.$$

This implies that g is continuous at x.

We may accordingly state the

Corollary 1

If f: $[a, b] \to$ R is continuous and of bounded variation, then $f = g - h$, where g and h are continuous and monotonically nondecreasing.

We also obtain, using Theorem 8, a result for functions of bounded variation which was obtained in Chapter 6 for monotonically nondecreasing functions.

Corollary 2

If $\{f_n\}$ is a uniformly bounded sequence of functions defined on $[a, b]$, with K as uniform bound, and there is an M such that $V(f_n; [a, b]) \leq M$, $n = 1, 2, \cdots$, then $\{f_n\}$ has a subsequence which converges everywhere on $[a, b]$ to a function f, with $V(f; [a, b]) \leq M$.

Proof

Let $f_n = g_n - h_n$, $n = 1, 2, \cdots$, be the decomposition of Theorem 8. Then $\{g_n\}$ is a sequence of monotonically nondecreasing functions, uniformly bounded by M, and $\{h_n\}$ is a sequence of monotonically nondecreasing functions, uniformly bounded by $M + K$.

Now, $\{f_n\}$ has a subsequence $\{f_{n_k}\}$ such that $\{g_{n_k}\}$ converges everywhere to a function g, and $\{f_{n_k}\}$ has a subsequence $\{f_{m_k}\}$ such that $\{h_{m_k}\}$ converges everywhere to a function h. So $\{f_{m_k}\}$ converges to $f = g - h$. That $V(f; [a, b]) \leq M$ is left to the reader.

9. DEFINITION OF RIEMANN STIELTJES INTEGRAL

We now define upper and lower integrals of a bounded function with respect to a monotonically nondecreasing function.

Accordingly let f be bounded and let g be monotonically nondecreasing on a closed interval $[a, b]$. For every partition $\pi = \{a = x_0 < x_1 < \cdots < x_n = b\}$ of $[a, b]$, let

$$u(f, g, \pi) = \sum_{i=1}^{n} \sup \{f(x)\colon x \in [x_{i-1}, x_i]\} \cdot [g(x_i) - g(x_{i-1})]$$

and

$$l(f, g, \pi) = \sum_{i=1}^{n} \inf \{f(x)\colon x \in [x_{i-1}, x_i]\} \cdot [g(x_i) - g(x_{i-1})].$$

Since the numbers $g(x_i) - g(x_{i-1})$ are nonnegative, $i = 1, \cdots, n$, it follows that $u(f, g, \pi) \geq l(f, g, \pi)$. It also follows, from the same fact, that if π and π' are partitions of I, with π a refinement of π', then

$$u(f, g, \pi) \leq u(f, g, \pi')$$

and

$$l(f, g, \pi) \geq l(f, g, \pi').$$

We then obtain, as for the Riemann integral, the fact that, for any partitions π_1 and π_2 of $[a, b]$,

$$l(f, g, \pi_1) \leq u(f, g, \pi_2).$$

This allows us to define **upper and lower integrals of f with respect to g as**

$$\overline{\int} f\, dg = \inf u(f, g, \pi)$$

and

$$\underline{\int} f\, dg = \sup l(f, g, \pi),$$

where the supremum and infinum are taken over all partitions π of $[a, b]$. Clearly,

$$\underline{\int} f\, dg \leq \overline{\int} f\, dg.$$

If the upper and lower integrals are equal, we say that the **Riemann Stieltjes integral of f with respect to g** exists, and write it as

$$\int f\, dg, \quad \text{or} \quad \int_a^b f\, dg.$$

The Riemann integral is the special case for which $g(x) = x$, for every $x \in [a, b]$.

Most of the elementary properties of the Riemann integral remain valid for this generalization, and we shall consider some of them as exercises.

We mention one property that fails to be extendable to this case. It is possible for f to be integrable with respect to g on intervals $[a, c]$ and $[c, b]$, but not on $[a, b]$. However, if either f or g is continuous, this property also holds.

We shall not consider the details of these matters in the text, but do prove the following result.

Theorem 9

If f is continuous on $[a, b]$, then f is integrable on $[a, b]$ with respect to every g which is monotonically nondecreasing on $[a, b]$.

Proof

Let f be continuous and g monotonically nondecreasing on $[a, b]$. Let $\epsilon > 0$. There is a $\delta > 0$ such that $x, y \in [a, b]$, $|x - y| < \delta$ implies $|f(x) - f(y)| < \epsilon$. Let $\pi = \{a = x_0 < x_1 < \cdots < x_n = b\}$ be a partition of $[a, b]$ of norm less than δ. Then

$$\begin{aligned} u(f, g, \pi) &- l(f, g, \pi) \\ &= \sum_{i=1}^{n} \sup\{f(x): x \in [x_{i-1}, x_i]\}[g(x_i) - g(x_{i-1})] \\ &\qquad - \sum_{i=1}^{n} \inf\{f(x): x \in [x_{i-1}, x_i]\}[g(x_i) - g(x_{i-1})] \\ &= \sum_{i=1}^{n}\Big(\sup\{f(x): x \in [x_{i-1}, x_i]\} \\ &\qquad - \inf\{f(x): x \in [x_{i-1}, x_i]\}\Big) \cdot [g(x_i) - g(x_{i-1})] \\ &\le \sum_{i=1}^{n} \epsilon[g(x_i) - g(x_{i-1})] = \epsilon[g(b) - g(a)]. \end{aligned}$$

It follows that $\overline{\int} f\,dg = \underline{\int} f\,dg$. ∎

Conversely, if f is not continuous on $[a, b]$, there is a monotonically nondecreasing g such that $\overline{\int} f\,dg > \underline{\int} f\,dg$.

Suppose f is not continuous at x_0. There are four possibilities. Let us consider the one for which there is a sequence $\{x_n\}$, $x_n > x_0$, $n = 1, 2, \cdots$, $\lim_n x_n = x_0$, for which $\lim_n f(x_n) > f(x_0) + k$, $k > 0$. In this case, consider the function g defined by

$$g(x) = \begin{cases} 0, & x \le x_0 \\ 1, & x > x_0. \end{cases}$$

Every partition π of $[a, b]$ has an interval $I = [c, d]$ which contains x_0 and points of $\{x_n\}$. Then

$$\sup \{f(x): x \in [c, d]\}[g(d) - g(c)] - \inf \{f(x): x \in [c, d]\}[g(d) - g(c)] > k.$$

It follows that

$$u(f, g, \pi) > l(f, g, \pi) + k$$

so that

$$\overline{\int} f\,dg > \underline{\int} f\,dg.$$

The argument for the other three cases is quite similar.

If g is of bounded variation on $[a, b]$, we consider its decomposition $g = g_1 - g_2$ of Theorem 8. We say that f is integrable with respect to g if it is integrable with respect to g_1 and g_2, and define

$$\int f\,dg = \int f\,dg_1 - \int f\,dg_2.$$

This integral still retains many properties of the Riemann integral. In particular, a continuous function is integrable with respect to every function of bounded variation.

EXERCISES

1.1 By taking the same partitions as in the example for x^2, show that

$$\int_0^t \sin x\,dt = 1 - \cos t.$$

1.2 In similar fashion, show that

$$\int_1^4 x^{-1/2}\,dx = 3.$$

1.3 If π is a refinement of π', show that $l(f, \pi) \geq l(f, \pi')$.

1.4 Show that if f is bounded on a closed interval $[a, b]$, then f is Riemann integrable if, and only if, for every $\epsilon > 0$ there is a partition π such that

$$u(f, \pi) < l(f, \pi) + \epsilon.$$

2.1 Show that the union of a finite number of sets of content zero is of content zero.

2.2 Give an example of an infinite set of content zero.

2.3 Give an example of an uncountable set of content zero.

2.4 If f is Riemann integrable on $[a, b]$, and F is defined as

$$F(x) = \int_a^x f,$$

for every $x \in [a, b]$, show that F is continuous.

2.5 If S has content zero, show that its image under a mapping which is differentiable, with continuous derivative, also has content zero.

3.1 By direct use of the definition, show that if f and g are Riemann integrable on $[a, b]$, then $f + g$ is Riemann integrable on $[a, b]$.

3.2 By direct use of the definition, show that if f and g are Riemann integrable on $[a, b]$, then fg is Riemann integrable on $[a, b]$.

3.3 By direct use of the definition, show that if f is Riemann integrable a $[a, b]$, then so is $|f|$.

3.4 By direct use of the definition, show that if f is Riemann integrable on $[a, b]$, and $1/f$ is bounded, then $1/f$ is Riemann integrable on $[a, b]$.

3.5 If f is Riemann integrable on $[a, b]$, show that

$$\left|\int_a^b f\right| \leq \int_a^b |f|.$$

4.1 Give the details showing that for

$$f(x) = \begin{cases} 1, & x \text{ rational} \\ 0, & x \text{ irrational,} \end{cases}$$

we have $\underline{\int} f = 0$ and $\overline{\int} f = 1$.

5.1 If f is monotonically nondecreasing and continuous and g is continuous on $[a, b]$, show that there is a $\xi \in (a, b)$ for which

$$\int_a^b fg = f(a)\int_a^\xi g + f(b)\int_\xi^b g.$$

5.2 If f is integrable on $[a, b]$, show that for every $\epsilon > 0$ there is a continuous g such that

$$\int_a^b |f - g| < \epsilon.$$

5.3 If f is integrable on $[a, b]$, and $0 < p < \infty$, show that for every $\epsilon > 0$ there is a continuous g on $[a, b]$ such that

$$\int_a^b |f - g|^p < \epsilon.$$

5.4 If f is integrable on $[a, b]$ and $\int_a^b f\varphi = 0$, for every infinitely differentiable φ which is zero outside of a closed interval $[c, d] \subset (a, b)$ (the $[c, d]$ depending on φ), show that f is zero, except perhaps on a set of content zero.

5.5 For f and g continuous and summable on $(-\infty, \infty)$, define $f*g$ by

$$(f*g)(x) = \int_{-\infty}^{\infty} f(x - y)g(y)\, dy.$$

Show that $f*g = g*f$.

5.6 Show that $f*g$ is continuous and summable and that

$$\int_{-\infty}^{\infty} |f*g| \leq \int_{-\infty}^{\infty} |f| \int_{-\infty}^{\infty} |g|.$$

5.7 If f is continuous and g is infinitely differentiable, show that $f*g$ is infinitely differentiable.

6.1 Discuss $\int_0^{\infty} x^r$ for all real r.

6.2 Show that $\int_0^{\infty} (\sin x)/x = \dfrac{\pi}{2}$.

6.3 Show that $\int_0^{\infty} e^{-x^2} = \dfrac{\pi}{2}$.

6.4 Evaluate $\int_a^b dx/[(x - a)(b - x)]$.

6.5 If f is bounded on (a, b) and is Riemann integrable on every closed subinterval of (a, b), then f is integrable on (a, b).

7.1 Show that the function f defined on $[-1, 1]$ by

$$f(x) = \begin{cases} x^2 \sin 1/x, & x \neq 0 \\ 0, & x = 0, \end{cases}$$

is of bounded variation.

7.2 Show that the function f defined on $[-1, 1]$ by

$$f(x) = \begin{cases} x \sin 1/x, & x \neq 0 \\ 0, & x = 0, \end{cases}$$

is not of bounded variation.

7.3 Show that if f is Riemann integrable on $[a, b]$ and $F(x) = \int_a^x f$, for every $x \in [a, b]$, then F is of bounded variation on $[a, b]$.

7.4 A function f is said to be Lipschitzian on an interval $[a, b]$ if there is an L such that $|f(y) - f(x)| \leq L\,|x - y|$, for every $x, y \in [a, b]$. Give an example of a function of bounded variation on $[a, b]$ which is not Lipschitzian on $[a, b]$.

7.5 Give an example of a function of bounded variation on $[a, b]$ which is not Lipschitzian on any subinterval of $[a, b]$.

7.6 For functions f and g, defined on an interval $[a, b]$, show that

$$V(f + g; [a, b]) \leq V(f; [a, b]) + V(g; [a, b]).$$

7.7 If f is defined on $[a, b]$, and $c \in [a, b]$ show that

$$V(f; [a, c]) + V(f; [c, b]) = V(f; [a, b]).$$

7.8 Give an example of a continuous function which is not of bounded variation in any interval.

8.1 Complete the proof of Corollary 2 to Theorem 8.

9.1 Give an example of a monotonically nondecreasing function g, and a function f, on $[-1, 1]$, such that f is integrable with respect to g on $[-1,0]$ and on $[0, 1]$ but not on $[-1, 1]$.

9.2 Prove that a function f on $[a, b]$ is integrable with respect to every continuous monotonically nondecreasing function on $[a, b]$ if and only if the set of points of discontinuity of f is countable.

9.3 If f_1 and f_2 are integrable with respect to a monotonically nondecreasing function f on $[a, b]$, show that $f_1 + f_2$ is integrable with respect to g and

$$\int_a^b (f_1 + f_2)\, dg = \int_a^b f_1\, dg + \int_a^b f_2\, dg.$$

9.4 If f is continuous and g is monotonically nondecreasing on $[a, b]$, show that there is a $\xi \in [a, b]$, with

$$\int_a^b f\, dg = f(\xi)[g(b) - g(a)].$$

9.5 If f is bounded and g is of bounded variation on $[a, b]$, then g has other representations $g = h_2 - h_1$ as a difference of monotonically nondecreasing functions. Show that

$$\int_a^b f\,dh_2 - \int_a^b f\,dh_1,$$

is independent of the choice of h_1 and h_2, provided $\int_a^b f\,dh_1$ and $\int_a^b f\,dh_2$ exist.

9.6 If g is of bounded variation on $[a, b]$, and f is integrable with respect to g, then

$$\left|\int_a^b f\,dg\right| \leq \sup\{|f(x)|: x \in [a, b]\}V(g; [a, b]).$$

9.7 If f is continuous and g is of bounded variation on $[a, b]$, show that the function F given by

$$F(x) = \int_a^x f\,dg,$$

for $x \in [a, b]$, is of bounded variation on $[a, b]$.

CHAPTER 9

POWER SERIES

1. INTERVAL OF CONVERGENCE

We observed in Chapter 6 that for some functions there are series of the form

$$a_0 + a_1 x + \cdots + a_n x^n + \cdots,$$

where the coefficients $a_0, a_1, \cdots, a_n, \cdots$, are real numbers, which converge to the given function, at least for some values of x. In this chapter, we present a systematic treatment of series of this type. Such series are called **power series.**

The reader should note that, at the outset, we do not associate the series with a function. We are taking the series itself as the primary object. If it converges on a set S, then it defines a function on S. We will then observe that the series is actually the Taylor series of the function to which it converges.

More generally, we may consider power series of the form

$$a_0 + a_1(x - a) + a_2(x - a)^2 + \cdots + a_n(x - a)^n + \cdots,$$

but they reduce to the special series

$$a_0 + a_1 x + \cdots + a_n x^n + \cdots$$

by the change of variable $\xi = x + a$. It is accordingly sufficient to suppose $a = 0$.

We first examine the set of points at which the series converges. At $x = 0$, the series converges to a_0. Thus, every power series converges at one point, $x = 0$, at least.

Example A Consider the series

$$1 + x + 2!\,x^2 + \cdots + n!\,x^n + \cdots.$$

Let $x \neq 0$. Then

$$\lim_n n!\,x^n = \infty.$$

Since the terms of the series do not converge to zero, for $x \neq 0$, this series converges only at $x = 0$.

Example B For every $r > 0$, the series

$$1 + \frac{x}{r} + \frac{x^2}{r^2} + \cdots + \frac{x^n}{r^n} + \cdots$$

converges for $|x| < r$ and diverges for $|x| \geq r$, since for every x it is a geometric series.

Example C We have already seen that the series

$$1 + x + \frac{x^2}{2!} + \cdots + \frac{x^n}{n!} + \cdots$$

converges for every x.

Returning to the general case, we suppose that the series

$$a_0 + a_1x + a_2x^2 + \cdots + a_nx^n + \cdots$$

converges at $x = x_0$. Let $|x_1| < |x_0|$. Then

$$\sum_{n=0}^{\infty} |a_nx_1^n| = \sum_{n=0}^{\infty} |a_nx_0^n| \left|\frac{x_1}{x_0}\right|^n.$$

Since the series $\sum_{n=0}^{\infty} a_nx_0^n$ converges, there is an M such that $|a_nx_0^n| \leq M$, for all $n = 0, 1, 2, \cdots$. It follows that

$$\sum_{n=0}^{\infty} |a_nx_1^n| \leq M \sum_{n=0}^{\infty} \left|\frac{x_1}{x_0}\right|^n < \infty,$$

since $\sum_{n=1}^{\infty} \left|\frac{x_1}{x_0}\right|^n$ is a geometric series with ratio less than 1.

This proves

Theorem 1
The series

$$a_0 + a_1x + a_2x^2 + \cdots + a_nx^n + \cdots$$

either

(a) *converges only for* $x = 0$,

(b) *converges absolutely for all real* x, *or*

(c) *there is an* $r > 0$ *such that the series converges absolutely when* $|x| < r$, *and diverges when* $|x| > r$.

The theorem says nothing about the behavior of the series at the end points $x = r$ and $x = -r$. As the following examples indicate, anything can happen at the end points.

Example D The series

$$1 + x + x^2 + \cdots + x^n + \cdots$$

converges for $|x| < 1$ and diverges for $|x| \geq 1$.

Example E The series

$$1 + x + \frac{x^2}{2} + \cdots + \frac{x^n}{n} + \cdots$$

converges for $-1 \leq x < 1$ and diverges everywhere else. The convergence at $x = -1$ is not absolute.

Example F The series

$$1 + x + \frac{x^2}{2^2} + \cdots + \frac{x^n}{n^2} + \cdots$$

converges absolutely for $|x| \leq 1$ and diverges for $|x| > 1$.

The number r of Theorem 1 is called the **radius of convergence** of the power series. The open interval $(-r, r)$ is called its **interval of convergence.** In Case **(a)**, we say that the radius of convergence is zero, and in Case **(b)** we say it is infinite.

One can easily find an expression for the radius of convergence in terms of the coefficients. The result we shall prove is the following:

If $\limsup_n \sqrt[n]{|a_n|} = 0$, then the radius of convergence is infinite.

If $\limsup_n \sqrt[n]{|a_n|} = \infty$, then the radius of convergence is zero.

If $\limsup_n \sqrt[n]{|a_n|} = 1/r$, $0 < r < \infty$, then the radius of convergence is r.

Suppose then that $\limsup_n \sqrt[n]{|a_n|} = 0$. For any x, it follows that

$$\limsup_n \sqrt[n]{|a_n x^n|} = |x| \limsup_n \sqrt[n]{|a_n|} = 0.$$

There is then an N such that $\sqrt[n]{|a_n x^n|} < 1/2$, for every $n > N$. Thus, $|a_n x^n| < (1/2)^n$, for every $n > N$. It follows that the series converges absolutely for every x.

Suppose $\limsup_n \sqrt[n]{|a_n|} = \infty$. For any $x \neq 0$,

$$\limsup_n \sqrt[n]{|a_n x^n|} = \infty.$$

This implies that $|a_n x^n| > 1$, for infinitely many values of n. Since the terms of the series do not converge to zero, the series diverges for every $x \neq 0$.

Suppose $0 < r < \infty$, and $\limsup_n \sqrt[n]{|a_n|} = 1/r$. Let $|x| < r$. There is an N and a k, with $0 < k < 1$, such that

$$\sqrt[n]{|a_n|}\,|x| < k$$

for all $n > N$. Then $|a_n x^n| < k^n$, for all $n > N$. Thus, the series converges absolutely at x. Let $|x| > r$. Then

$$\sqrt[n]{|a_n|}\,|x| > 1$$

for infinitely many values of n. Moreover, $|a_n x^n| > 1$, for these values of n. Thus the series diverges at x since its terms do not converge to zero.

We have thus proved

Theorem 2

The radius of convergence r of the power series

$$a_0 + a_1 x + a_2 x^2 + \cdots + a_n x^n + \cdots$$

is given by

$$\frac{1}{r} = \limsup_n \sqrt[n]{|a_n|},$$

if $0 < \limsup_n \sqrt[n]{|a_n|} < \infty$.

If $\limsup_n \sqrt[n]{|a_n|} = 0$, *the radius of convergence is infinite.*

If $\limsup_n \sqrt[n]{|a_n|} = \infty$, *the radius of convergence is zero.*

2. THE FUNCTION DEFINED BY A POWER SERIES

A power series converges to a function on its interval of convergence, and perhaps at the end points. The convergence is absolute on the open interval. It need not be absolute at an endpoint, as Example E shows, even if it converges there. Let

$$a_0 + a_1x + \cdots + a_nx^n + \cdots$$

have radius of convergence r. Let $K \subset (-r, r)$ be a compact set. We show that the series converges absolutely uniformly on K. The proof is like the one given to establish the existence of the interval of convergence, but we give the details because of the great importance of the result.

There is a $k > 0$ such that $k < r$ but $|x| \leq k$ for every $x \in K$. Let ρ be such that $k < \rho < r$. Then, for all $x \in K$,

$$\sum_{n=0}^{\infty} |a_nx^n| < \sum_{n=0}^{\infty} |a_n| \rho^n \left|\frac{x}{\rho}\right|^n \leq \sum_{n=0}^{\infty} |a_n| \rho^n \left|\frac{k}{\rho}\right|^n.$$

The series on the right converges since $\{|a_n| \rho^n\}$ is bounded and $\left|\frac{k}{\rho}\right| < 1$.

It follows that the power series converges absolutely uniformly on K.

Theorem 3

The series $\sum_{n=0}^{\infty} a_nx^n$ *converges absolutely uniformly on every compact subset of its interval of convergence. In particular, it converges absolutely uniformly on every closed subinterval of its interval of convergence.*

This theorem has the important

Corollary

The function f to which a power series $\sum_{n=0}^{\infty} a_nx^n$ *converges, on its interval* $J = (-r, r)$ *of convergence, is a continuous function.*

Proof

Let $x \in J$. Then x is the center of a closed interval on which $\sum_{n=0}^{\infty} a_n x^n$ converges uniformly to f. But the terms of the series are continuous functions, so that the sum is also continuous. ∎

The function f, defined by a power series on its interval of convergence, is not merely continuous. We proceed to show that it is infinitely differentiable.

We first show that a power series and the associated series obtained by term-by-term differentiation have the same interval of convergence.

Accordingly, along with the series

$$a_0 + a_1 x + \cdots + a_n x^n + \cdots,$$

we consider the differentiated series

$$a_1 + 2a_2 x + \cdots + n a_n x^{n-1} + \cdots.$$

Let r and r' be the respective radii of convergence of the two series. We show that $r = r'$.

Suppose $x_0 \neq 0$ and that the series

$$a_0 + a_1 x_0 + \cdots + a_n x_0^n + \cdots$$

converges. Let x_1 be such that $0 < |x_1| < |x_0|$. Then

$$\begin{aligned}
&|a_1| + 2\,|a_2 x_1| + \cdots + n\,|a_n x_1^{n-1}| + \cdots \\
&= \frac{1}{|x_1|}\left\{|a_1 x_0| \left|\frac{x_1}{x_0}\right| + 2\,|a_2 x_0^2| \left|\frac{x_1}{x_0}\right|^2 + \cdots + n\,|a_n x_0^n| \left|\frac{x_1}{x_0}\right|^n + \cdots\right\} \\
&\le \frac{M}{|x_1|}\left\{\left|\frac{x_1}{x_0}\right| + 2\left|\frac{x_1}{x_0}\right|^2 + \cdots + n\left|\frac{x_1}{x_0}\right|^n + \cdots\right\},
\end{aligned}$$

where $|a_n x_0^n| \le M$, for every $n = 1, 2, \cdots$.

But the ratio test shows that the series $\sum_{n=1}^{\infty} n \left|\frac{x_1}{x_0}\right|^n$ converges. It follows that $r' \ge r$.

The proof that $r' \le r$ is easier, and is left to the reader.

What we have shown is that a power series has the same radius of convergence as its differentiated series. In the same way, the differentiated series has the same radius of convergence as its differentiated series, so that the original series has the same radius of convergence as its twice differentiated series. By continuing, we obtain the result that for every $m = 1, 2, \cdots$, the power series has the same radius of convergence as its m times differentiated series. Thus, on its interval of convergence, the power series converges to a function f, and for every $m = 1, 2, \cdots$, its m times differentiated series converges to a function f_m.

Let us emphasize that what we have proved relates only to the series, not to the function f to which it converges. We do not yet know that f is differentiable, let alone that the differentiated series converges to the derivative of f.

We shall prove that all this is indeed true. We show that f is differentiable on the interval of convergence of the series and that its derivative f' is equal to f_1, the sum of the differentiated series. It then follows that, for every $m = 1, 2, \cdots, f$ is m times differentiable and $f^{(m)} = f_m$.

Let $\sum_{n=0}^{\infty} a_n x^n$ have $(-r, r)$ as its interval of convergence, and let $f(x) = \sum_{n=0}^{\infty} a_n x^n$ on $(-r, r)$. The series $\sum_{n=1}^{\infty} n a_n x^{n-1}$ also has $(-r, r)$ as its interval of convergence. Let $f_1(x) = \sum_{n=1}^{\infty} n a_n x^{n-1}$ on $(-r, r)$.

For every $n = 1, 2, \cdots$, let

$$s_n(x) = \sum_{k=0}^{n} a_k x^k$$

and

$$t_n(x) = \sum_{k=1}^{n} k a_k x^{k-1}.$$

Evidently,

$$s_n' = t_n$$

on $(-r, r)$ for every $n = 1, 2, \cdots$.

On every closed interval $I \subset (-r, r)$, $\{s_n\}$ converges uniformly to f and $\{t_n\}$ converges uniformly to f_1. By Theorem 7, Chapter 8, it follows that f is differentiable and $f' = f_1$ on $(-r, r)$. We have proved

Theorem 4

If the series $\sum_{n=0}^{\infty} a_n x^n$ has $J = (-r, r)$ as its interval of convergence and converges to f on J, then f is infinitely differentiable on J. Moreover, the series $\sum_{n=1}^{\infty} n a_n x^{n-1}$ converges to f' on J, the series $\sum_{n=2}^{\infty} n(n-1) a_n x^{n-2}$ converges to $f^{(2)}$ on J, and for every $k = 3, 4, \cdots$ the series $\sum_{n=k}^{\infty} n(n-1) \cdots (n-k+1) a_n x^{n-k}$ converges to $f^{(k)}$ on J.

3. FURTHER PROPERTIES OF POWER SERIES

Let $\sum_{n=0}^{\infty} a_n x^n$ converge to the function f on its interval $J = (-r, r)$ of convergence. We shall compute the coefficients $a_0, a_1, \cdots, a_n, \cdots$ in terms of f.

Since

$$f(x) = a_0 + a_1 x + \cdots + a_n x^n + \cdots$$

on J, it follows that

$$a_0 = f(0).$$

Since

$$f'(x) = a_1 + 2a_2 x + \cdots + n a_n x^{n-1} + \cdots$$

on J, it follows that

$$a_1 = f'(0).$$

Since

$$f^{(2)}(x) = 2a_2 + 3 \cdot 2a_3 x + \cdots + n(n-1)a_n x^{n-2} + \cdots$$

on J, it follows that

$$a_2 = \frac{1}{2!} f^{(2)}(0).$$

By induction, for every $n = 1, 2, \cdots,$

$$a_n = \frac{1}{n!} f^{(n)}(0).$$

The power series which converges to f is thus given by

$$f(0) + f'(0)x + f^{(2)}(0)\frac{x^2}{2!} + \cdots + f^{(n)}(0)\frac{x^n}{n!} + \cdots.$$

We thus have

Theorem 5

If a power series $\sum_{n=0}^{\infty} a_n x^n$ has a nonzero interval of convergence J, and converges to f on J, the series is the Taylor series

$$f'(0) + f'(0)x + f^{(2)}(0)\frac{x^2}{2!} + \cdots + f^{(n)}(0)\frac{x^n}{n!} + \cdots$$

of the function f.

Theorem 5 implies that a function f defined by a power series is determined everywhere by its value and the values of its derivatives at the single point $x = 0$. Another way of saying this is that if a function is given by a power series in an interval, no matter how large, its values everywhere on the interval are determined by the values on any interval containing zero, no matter how small.

Of course, we cannot completely prescribe the derivatives at $x = 0$. Indeed, we know that in order for the radius of convergence to be positive, the condition $\limsup_n \sqrt[n]{|a_n|} < \infty$ must be satisfied.

It can be shown, but we shall not do it here, that for any sequence

$$b_0, b_1, \cdots, b_n, \cdots$$

of real numbers, there is an infinitely differentiable function f for which

$$f(0) = b_0, \qquad f'(0) = b_1, \cdots, \qquad f^{(n)}(0) = b_n, \cdots.$$

This again shows the existence of infinitely differentiable functions which may not be represented by power series.

Although the behavior of a power series in its interval of convergence is the best that can be expected, its behavior at the end points of its interval of convergence is unpredictable. Yet, even in this case, something good can be said. Let $\sum_{n=0}^{\infty} a_n x^n$ converge on $(-r, r)$ and suppose $\sum_{n=0}^{\infty} a_n r^n$ converges. We shall show that

$$\lim_{x \to r} \sum_{n=0}^{\infty} a_n x^n = \sum_{n=0}^{\infty} a_n r^n.$$

Thus if the series $\sum_{n=0}^{\infty} a_n x^n$ converges to a function f on $(-r, r]$, then f is continuous on this semiopen interval.

For simplicity, we may assume that $r = 1$. Let $s = \sum_{n=0}^{\infty} a_n = f(1)$ and $s_n = \sum_{k=0}^{n} a_k$, $n = 0, 1, 2, \cdots$.

Then, for $0 < x < 1$, we have

$$|f(1) - f(x)| = \left| \sum_{n=0}^{\infty} a_n - \sum_{n=0}^{\infty} a_n x^n \right|$$
$$= \left| s - \sum_{n=0}^{\infty} s_n (1 - x) x^n \right|.$$

Since, for $0 < x < 1$,

$$\sum_{n=0}^{\infty} (1 - x) x^n = 1,$$

we have

$$|f(1) - f(x)| = \left| \sum_{n=0}^{\infty} (s - s_n)(1 - x) x^n \right|.$$

Let $\epsilon > 0$. There is an N such that $n > N$ implies $|s - s_n| < \epsilon/2$. Now,

$$|f(1) - f(x)| \leq \sum_{n=1}^{N} |s - s_n| (1 - x)x^n + \sum_{n=N+1}^{\infty} |s - s_n| (1 - x)x^n$$
$$\leq \sum_{n=1}^{N} |s - s_n| (1 - x)x^n + \epsilon/2, \qquad \text{for every positive } x < 1.$$

But there is a $\delta > 0$ such that $1 - x < \delta$ implies

$$\sum_{n=1}^{N} |s - s_n| (1 - x)x^n < \frac{\epsilon}{2}.$$

Thus,

$$\lim_{x\to 1} f(x) = f(1),$$

and we have proved the Abel theorem on continuity of power series.

Theorem 6

If the series $\sum_{n=0}^{\infty} a_n x^n$ *converges to the function* $f(x)$, *for* $|x| < 1$, *and the series* $\sum_{n=0}^{\infty} a_n$ *converges, then*

$$\sum_{n=0}^{\infty} a_n = \lim_{x\to 1} f(x).$$

A series $\sum_{n=0}^{\infty} a_n$ is said to be **Abel summable,** to a value s, if the associated power series $\sum_{n=0}^{\infty} a_n x^n$ converges for $|x| < 1$ to a function f and

$$\lim_{x\to 1} f(x) = s.$$

Theorem 6 asserts that if a series $\sum_{n=0}^{\infty} a_n$ converges and has sum equal to s, then it is Abel summable to s. Moreover, there are divergent series which are Abel summable.

Example Consider the series

$$1 - 1 + 1 - 1 + \cdots.$$

The associated power series is $\sum_{n=0}^{\infty} (-1)^n x^n$. This series converges on $(-1, 1)$ to the function f given by

$$f(x) = \frac{1}{1 + x}.$$

Since $\lim_{x\to 1} 1/(1 + x) = 1/2$, the series is Abel summable to $1/2$.

However, certain conditions on the terms a_n, $n = 0, 1, 2, \cdots$, together with Abel summability of a series $\sum_{n=0}^{\infty} a_n$, assure convergence. Such a condition is that the sequence $\{na_n\}$ be bounded. This is a difficult fact to prove. We shall prove the easier

Theorem 7

If $\sum_{n=0}^{\infty} a_n x^n$ *is Abel summable to* s *and* $\lim_n na_n = 0$, *then* $\sum_{n=0}^{\infty} a_n$ *converges to* s.

Proof

We assume $\sum_{n=0}^{\infty} a_n x^n = f(x)$ on $(-1, 1)$ and that $\lim_{x \to 1} f(x) = s$.

We shall use the easy-to-prove facts that, for $0 < x < 1$, $(1 - x)^k \leq k(1 - x)$, and that $\sum_{k=n+1}^{\infty} x^k \leq 1/(1 - x)$.

In addition, since the convergence of a sequence $\{t_n\}$ implies that of $\{(t_1 + \cdots + t_n)/n\}$ and to the same limit, the assumption $\lim_n na_n = 0$ implies $\lim_n (1/n) \sum_{k=1}^{n} k\,|a_k| = 0$.

Now, for every n, if $s_n = a_0 + a_1 + \cdots + a_n$,

$$s_n - s = \sum_{k=0}^{n} a_k - s + f(x) - \sum_{k=0}^{\infty} a_k x^k$$

$$= f(x) - s + \sum_{k=1}^{n} a_k(1 - x^k) - \sum_{k=n+1}^{\infty} a_k x^k.$$

Then, for $0 < x < 1$,

$$|s_n - s| \leq |f(x) - s| + \sum_{k=1}^{n} k\,|a_k|\,(1 - x) + 1/n \sum_{k=n+1}^{\infty} k\,|a_k|\,x^k$$

Let $\epsilon > 0$. There is an N such that $n > N$ implies

$$\left| f\left(1 - \frac{1}{n}\right) - s \right| \leq \epsilon, \qquad n\,|a_n| < \epsilon \quad \text{and} \quad \frac{1}{n} \sum_{k=1}^{n} k\,|a_k| < \epsilon.$$

For $n > N$ and $x = 1 - 1/n$,

$$|s_n - s| \leq \epsilon + n \cdot \frac{1}{n} \epsilon + \frac{1}{n} \cdot \epsilon \cdot \frac{1}{1/n} = 3\epsilon. \quad \blacksquare$$

EXERCISES

2.1 In the notation of the text, show that $r' \geq r$.

2.2 Show that the function defined by a power series is determined by its values on any set which has zero as a limit point.

2.3 Show that the power series, obtained, from a given power series by term by term integration, has the same radius of convergence and converges to the integral of the function to which the original series converges.

3.1 Define the product of two power series and show that its interval of convergence contains the intersection of the intervals of convergence of the two given series.

3.2 Show that if $a_0 \neq 0$ and the series $\sum_{n=0}^{\infty} a_n x^n$ has a positive radius of convergence, there is a unique power series $\sum_{n=0}^{\infty} b_n x^n$, with a positive radius of convergence such that $\sum_{n=0}^{\infty} a_n x^n \sum_{n=0}^{\infty} b_n x^n = 1$.

3.3 What can be said concerning the radius of convergence of $\sum_{n=0}^{\infty} a_n b^n$.

3.4 Obtain a power series expansion for $(x + a)^{1/2}$, $a \neq 0$. Determine the values of x for which it converges.

3.5 Determine the inverse series of the power series for $\cos x$.

3.6 Determine the inverse series of the power series for $\dfrac{\sin x}{x}$.

3.7 Using power series, prove that

$$\sin (x + y) = \sin x \cos y + \cos x \sin y.$$

3.8 Obtain a binomial theorem for the case where the exponent is a negative integer.

3.9 Using the fact that

$$\tan^{-1} x = \int_0^x \frac{dt}{1 + t^2},$$

evaluate π to 4 decimals.

3.10 Using power series, find a class of solutions to the differential equation

$$y' - y = 0.$$

3.11 Using power series, find a class of solutions to the differential equation

$$y'' + y = 0.$$

CHAPTER 10

FOURIER SERIES

1. ORTHONORMAL SYSTEMS

We turn from a study of functions which may be obtained as the sum of a series

$$a_0 + a_1x + a_2x^2 + \cdots + a_nx^n + \cdots$$

to those which may be obtained as the sum of a series

$$a_0 + \sum_{n=1}^{\infty} (a_n \cos nx + b_n \sin nx).$$

Such a series is called a trigonometric series.

While, as we have seen, the theory of power series is simple, and the functions which may be represented as power series have regular behavior, (in particular, they are infinitely differentiable), the theory of trigonometric series is difficult and complicated. We shall, accordingly, be able to present only the most elementary aspects of this theory.

Some of the simplest properties of trigonometric series follow from the fact that the trigonometric functions form an orthonormal system, and these properties are valid for orthonormal systems in general.

If $I = [a, b]$ is a closed interval, a sequence $\{\phi_n\}$ of Riemann integrable functions on I is called **orthogonal** if

$$\int_a^b \phi_n\phi_m = 0, \quad \text{if} \quad n \neq m.$$

If, in addition, for every $n = 1, 2, \cdots$,

$$\int_a^b \phi_n^2 = 1,$$

the system is called **orthonormal.**

Example A The functions

$$\frac{1}{2\pi}, \qquad \frac{1}{\pi}\cos nx, \qquad \frac{1}{\pi}\sin nx, \qquad n = 1, 2, \cdots$$

form an orthonormal system for the interval $[-\pi, \pi]$.

We leave the verification to the reader.

Example B The functions

$$\frac{2}{\pi}\sin nx, \qquad n = 1, 2, \cdots,$$

form an orthonormal system for the interval $[0, \pi]$.

There are many orthonormal systems of polynomials and other functions, but we shall not consider these special systems here.

Suppose $\{\phi_n\}$ is an orthonormal system of continuous functions on an interval $[a, b]$, and that a series

$$a_1\phi_1 + a_2\phi_2 + \cdots + a_n\phi_n + \cdots$$

converges uniformly to a function f on $[a, b]$. Then f is continuous on $[a, b]$. We compute the coefficients of the series in terms of f. For every n, the series

$$a_1\phi_1\phi_n + a_2\phi_2\phi_n + \cdots + a_n\phi_n\phi_n + \cdots$$

converges uniformly to $f\phi_n$. Then

$$\int_a^b f\phi_n = \int_a^b a_1\phi_1\phi_n + \int_a^b a_2\phi_2\phi_n + \cdots + \int_a^b a_n\phi_n\phi_n + \cdots$$

Since $\{\phi_n\}$ is orthonormal, we obtain

$$a_n = \int_a^b f\phi_n.$$

Theorem 1

If $\{\phi_n\}$ is an orthonormal system of continuous functions on an interval $[a, b]$ and a series $\sum_{n=1}^{\infty} a_n\phi_n$ converges uniformly to a function f on $[a, b]$, then

$$a_n = \int_a^b f\phi_n, \qquad n = 1, 2, \cdots.$$

This suggests that we associate with every Riemann integrable function f on $[a, b]$, the series

$$\phi_1\int_a^b f\phi_1 + \phi_2\int_a^b f\phi_2 + \cdots + \phi_n\int_a^b f\phi_n + \cdots,$$

where we have written the coefficients to the right for the sake of appearance. This series is called the **Fourier series** of f with respect to the system $\{\phi_n\}$.

We know that if a series in $\{\phi_n\}$ converges uniformly to a function f, it is the Fourier series of f. We note that we do not know, however, whether or not the Fourier series of a function need converge to the function.

We shall deal only with Fourier series. We first prove

Theorem 2 (Bessel's inequality)

If f is Riemann integrable on $[a, b]$, $\{\phi_n\}$ is an orthonormal system on $[a, b]$, and $\sum_{n=1}^{\infty} a_n\phi_n$ is the Fourier series of f, then

$$\int_a^b f^2 \geq \sum_{n=1}^{\infty} a_n^2.$$

Proof

For every $n = 1, 2, \cdots,$

$$\int_a^b \left(\sum_{k=1}^{n} a_k\phi_k\right)^2 = \int_a^b \sum_{k,l=1}^{n} a_k a_l \phi_k \phi_l = \sum_{k,l=1}^{n} \int_a^b a_k a_l \phi_k \phi_l = \sum_{k=1}^{n} a_k^2.$$

Thus,

$$0 \leq \int_a^b \left(f - \sum_{k=1}^{n} a_k\phi_k\right)^2 = \int_a^b f^2 - 2\sum_{k=1}^{n} a_k \int_a^b f\phi_k$$
$$+ \int_a^b \left(\sum_{k=1}^{n} a_k\phi_k\right)^2 = \int_a^b f^2 - 2\sum_{k=1}^{n} a_k^2 + \sum_{k=1}^{n} a_k^2.$$

Then,

$$\int_a^b f^2 \geq \sum_{k=1}^{n} a_k^2.$$

Since this inequality holds for every n, we have

$$\int_a^b f^2 \geq \sum_{n=1}^{\infty} a_n^2.$$

Corollary

If f is Riemann integrable on $[a, b]$, and $\sum_{n=1}^{\infty} a_n\phi_n$ is its Fourier series with respect to an orthonormal system $\{\phi_n\}$ on $[a, b]$, then

$$\lim_n a_n = 0.$$

In particular, not every series $\sum_{n=1}^{\infty} a_n\phi_n$ is the Fourier series of a Riemann integrable f.

We conclude this section with two facts which we shall need.

Schwarz Inequality. If f and g are Riemann integrable on $[a, b]$, then

$$\left(\int_a^b |fg|\right)^2 \leq \int_a^b f^2 \int_a^b g^2.$$

Proof

If either $\int_a^b f^2 = 0$ or $\int_a^b g^2 = 0$, then $\int_a^b |fg| = 0$, and the result holds. Suppose $\int_a^b f^2 \neq 0$ and $\int_a^b g^2 \neq 0$. For every real k,

$$0 \leq \int_a^b (|f| - k\,|g|)^2 = \int_a^b f^2 - 2k \int_a^b |fg| + k^2 \int_a^b g^2.$$

Let $k^2 = \dfrac{\int_a^b f^2}{\int_a^b g^2}$. Then

$$\left(\int_a^b |fg|\right)^2 \leq \int_a^b f^2 \int_a^b g^2. \quad ▌$$

Triangle Inequality. If f and g are Riemann integrable on $[a, b]$, then

$$\left[\int_a^b (f+g)^2\right]^{1/2} \leq \left[\int_a^b f^2\right]^{1/2} + \left[\int_a^b g^2\right]^{1/2}.$$

Proof

By the Schwarz inequality,

$$\begin{aligned}
\int_a^b (f+g)^2 &= \int_a^b f^2 + 2\int_a^b fg + \int_a^b g^2 \\
&\leq \int_a^b f^2 + 2\left[\int_a^b f^2\right]^{1/2}\left[\int_a^b g^2\right]^{1/2} + \int_a^b g^2 \\
&= \left(\left[\int_a^b f^2\right]^{1/2} + \left[\int_a^b g^2\right]^{1/2}\right)^2,
\end{aligned}$$

and the result follows. ▌

2. EXAMPLES OF FOURIER SERIES

We shall be concerned only with the orthonormal system of trigonometric functions on $[-\pi, \pi]$. It will be understood that all functions f considered satisfy $f(-\pi) = f(\pi)$ so that they may be extended by periodicity to the entire real line, or any subinterval thereof. We write the Fourier series of a Riemann integrable f as

$$\frac{a_0}{2} + \sum_{n=1}^{\infty} (a_n \cos nx + b_n \sin nx),$$

where

$$a_0 = \frac{1}{\pi}\int_{-\pi}^{\pi} f(t)\, dt,$$

$$a_n = \frac{1}{\pi}\int_{-\pi}^{\pi} f(t) \cos nt\, dt,$$

$$b_n = \frac{1}{\pi}\int_{-\pi}^{\pi} f(t) \sin nt\, dt, \qquad n = 1, 2, \cdots.$$

Example A Let

$$f(x) = \begin{cases} 0 & -\pi \leq x \leq 0 \\ 1 & 0 < x < \pi \\ 0 & x = \pi. \end{cases}$$

We obtain the Fourier series of f.

$$a_0 = \frac{1}{\pi}\int_{0}^{\pi} dt = 1$$

$$a_n = \frac{1}{\pi}\int_{0}^{\pi} \cos nt\, dt = 0, \quad n = 1, 2, \cdots.$$

$$b_n = \frac{1}{\pi}\int_{0}^{\pi} \sin nt\, dt = \begin{cases} 0, & n \text{ even} \\ \dfrac{2}{n\pi}, & n \text{ odd.} \end{cases}$$

The Fourier series of f is thus

$$\frac{1}{2} + \sum_{n=1}^{\infty} \frac{1}{n\pi} \sin 2nx.$$

Example B Let

$$f(x) = |x|, \qquad -\pi \leq x \leq \pi.$$

The Fourier coefficients of f are then

$$a_0 = \frac{1}{\pi}\int_{-\pi}^{\pi} |t|\, dt = \frac{2}{\pi}\int_{0}^{\pi} t\, dt = \pi,$$

$$a_n = \frac{1}{\pi}\int_{-\pi}^{\pi} |t| \cos nt\, dt = \frac{2}{\pi}\int_{0}^{\pi} t \cos nt\, dt = \begin{cases} -\dfrac{4}{n^2}, & n \text{ odd} \\ 0, & n \text{ even,} \end{cases}$$

$$b_n = \frac{1}{\pi}\int_{-\pi}^{\pi} |t| \sin n\, dt\, dt = 0, \qquad n = 1, 2, \cdots.$$

The Fourier series of f is thus

$$\frac{\pi}{2} - \frac{4}{\pi}\left(\cos x + \frac{\cos 3x}{9} + \frac{\cos 5x}{25} + \cdots\right).$$

This series converges uniformly absolutely to a function g. By Theorem 1, it is the Fourier series of g. It is also the Fourier series of f. This raises an important question. Can different continuous functions have the same Fourier series? We shall show in the next section that this is impossible. Assuming we know this, it follows that

$$|x| = \frac{\pi}{2} - \frac{4}{\pi}\left(\cos x + \frac{\cos 3x}{9} + \frac{\cos 5x}{25} + \cdots\right),$$

the convergence being uniform. Letting $x = 0$, we have

$$\frac{\pi^2}{8} = 1 + \frac{1}{3^2} + \frac{1}{5^2} + \cdots.$$

Example C Let

$$f(x) = \begin{cases} x, & -\pi \leq x < \pi, \\ -\pi, & x = \pi. \end{cases}$$

The Fourier coefficients of f are given by

$$a_0 = \frac{1}{\pi}\int_{-\pi}^{\pi} t\,dt = 0.$$

$$a_n = \frac{1}{\pi}\int_{-\pi}^{\pi} t\cos nt\,dt = 0$$

$$b_n = \frac{1}{\pi}\int_{-\pi}^{\pi} t\sin nt\,dt = \frac{2}{\pi}\int_{0}^{\pi} t\sin nt\,dt$$

$$= \frac{2(-1)^{n-1}}{n}, \qquad n = 1, 2, \cdots.$$

The Fourier series of f is then

$$2\left(\sin x - \frac{\sin 2x}{2} + \frac{\sin 3x}{3} - \cdots\right).$$

3. COMPLETENESS OF THE TRIGONOMETRIC SYSTEM

We make some remarks about orthonormal systems in general.

Let $[a, b]$ be a closed interval, and let $\{\phi_n\}$ be an orthonormal system on $[a, b]$. We have already noted that for every Riemann integrable f on $[a, b]$,

$$\int_a^b f^2 \geq \sum_{n=1}^{\infty} a_n^2,$$

where $a_1, a_2, \cdots$ are the Fourier coefficients of f with respect to the system $\{\phi_n\}$.

We wish to compare several important properties which an orthonormal system $\{\phi_n\}$ on an interval may have.

(a) For every Riemann integrable f on $[a, b]$, there is, for every $\epsilon > 0$, a finite linear combination,

$$g = c_1\phi_1 + \cdots + c_n\phi_n,$$

such that

$$\int_a^b (f - g)^2 < \epsilon.$$

(b) For every Riemann integrable f on $[a, b]$, with Fourier coefficients $a_1, a_2, \cdots, a_n, \cdots$, we have

$$\int_a^b f^2 = \sum_{n-1}^{\infty} a_n^2.$$

(c) If f is Riemann integrable on $[a, b]$, and its Fourier coefficients are all zero, then

$$\int_a^b f^2 = 0.$$

(d) For every Riemann integrable f on $[a, b]$, with Fourier coefficients $a_1, a_2, \cdots, a_n, \cdots$, we have

$$\lim_n \int_a^b \left(f - \sum_{i=1}^{n} a_i\phi_i\right)^2 = 0.$$

The following lemma is basic to this study.

Lemma

If f is Riemann integrable on $[a, b]$ and has Fourier coefficients $a_1, a_2, \cdots, a_n, \cdots$, then for every n, and any real numbers $c_1, \cdots, c_n$, we have

$$\int_a^b \left(f - \sum_{i=1}^n a_i\phi_i\right)^2 \leq \int_a^b \left(f - \sum_{i=1}^n c_i\phi_i\right)^2,$$

where $\{\phi_n\}$ is an orthonormal system on $[a, b]$.

Proof

We compute

$$\begin{aligned}\int_a^b \left(f - \sum_{i=1}^n c_i\phi_i\right)^2 &= \int_a^b f^2 - 2\sum_{i=1}^n a_ic_i + \sum_{i=1}^n c_i^2 \\ &= \int_a^b f^2 + \sum_{i=1}^n (a_i - c_i)^2 - \sum_{i=1}^n a_i^2 \geq \int_a^b f^2 - \sum_{i=1}^n a_i^2 \\ &= \int_a^b \left(f - \sum_{i=1}^n a_i\phi_i\right)^2. \quad \blacksquare\end{aligned}$$

We call an orthonormal system $\{\phi_n\}$ on an interval $[a, b]$ **closed** if for every $\epsilon > 0$ there is a finite linear combination

$$g = c_1\phi_1 + \cdots + c_n\phi_n$$

such that

$$\int_a^b (f - g)^2 < \epsilon.$$

As an immediate consequence of the lemma, we have the

Corollary 1

If the orthonormal system $\{\phi_n\}$ on $[a, b]$ is closed, then for every Riemann integrable f on $[a, b]$, we have

$$\lim_n \int_a^b \left(f - \sum_{i=1}^n a_i\phi_i\right)^2 = 0,$$

where $\sum_{n=1}^{\infty} a_n\phi_n$ is the Fourier series of f.

We may state this result in a different form as the

Corollary 2

If the orthonormal system $\{\phi_n\}$ on $[a, b]$ is closed then, for every Riemann integrable f on $[a, b]$, we have

$$\int_a^b f^2 = \sum_{n=1}^{\infty} a_n^2.$$

Proof

We recall that

$$\int_a^b \left(f - \sum_{i=1}^{n} a_i\phi_i\right)^2 = \int_a^b f^2 - \sum_{i=1}^{n} a_i^2,$$

so that the result follows from Corollary 1. ∎

We also obtain, with little effort, the

Corollary 3

If the orthonormal system $\{\phi_n\}$ on $[a, b]$ is closed, then a Riemann integrable f has all of its Fourier coefficients equal to zero if and only if

$$\int_a^b f^2 = 0.$$

An orthonormal system $\{\phi_n\}$ on $[a, b]$ is called complete if and only if all Riemann integrable functions f, which have Fourier coefficients all zero, satisfy $\int_a^b f^2 = 0$.

Every closed orthonormal system is complete.

If $\{\phi_n\}$ is complete and f and g have the same Fourier series with respect to $\{\phi_n\}$, then $f - g$ has all Fourier coefficients equal to zero. Thus, $\int_a^b (f - g)^2 = 0$. In particular, if f and g are also continuous, then $f = g$.

We show that the trigonometric functions are closed on $[-\pi, \pi]$.

In dealing with trigonometric Fourier series, we refer to the interval $[-\pi, \pi]$. However, since all functions considered are periodic of period 2π, they are defined by periodicity for all real numbers and we shall feel free to consider functions at points $x \in [-\pi, \pi]$. We may also consider the domain of the functions to be the boundary of the unit circle $x^2 + y^2 = 1$, and this interpretation is to be preferred for many purposes. However, we shall not be involved in such matters.

We first prove the

Lemma 2

For a quasilinear function g, of period 2π, on $[-\pi, \pi]$, the Fourier coefficients satisfy the condition

$$\sum_{n=1}^{\infty} (|a_n| + |b_n|) < \infty.$$

Proof

Using the formula for integration by parts, we obtain

$$a_n = \frac{1}{\pi}\int_{-\pi}^{\pi} g(t)\cos nt\,dt = \frac{1}{n\pi} g(t)\sin nt\Big|_{\pi}^{-\pi} - \frac{1}{n\pi}\int_{-\pi}^{\pi} g'(t)\sin nt\,dt$$

$$= -\frac{1}{n\pi}\int_{-\pi}^{\pi} g'(t)\sin nt\,dt.$$

Similarly,

$$b_n = \frac{1}{n\pi}\int_{-\pi}^{\pi} g'(t)\cos nt.$$

The derivative g' of g is a step function, defined everywhere except at a finite number of points. Its Fourier coefficients are given by

$$\alpha_n = nb_n, \qquad \beta_n = -na_n.$$

Since $\int_a^b (g')^2 \geq \sum_{n=1}^{\infty} (\alpha_n^2 + \beta_n^2)$, we have

$$\sum_{n=1}^{\infty} (\alpha_n^2 + \beta_n^2) < \infty.$$

Now,

$$0 \leq \left(|\alpha_n| - \frac{1}{n}\right)^2 + \left(|\beta_n| - \frac{1}{n}\right)^2$$

$$= \alpha_n^2 + \beta_n^2 + \frac{2}{n^2} - \frac{2}{n}(|\alpha_n| + |\beta_n|).$$

It follows that

$$|a_n| + |b_n| = \frac{1}{n}(|\alpha_n| + |\beta_n|) \leq \tfrac{1}{2}(\alpha_n^2 + \beta_n^2) + \frac{1}{n^2},$$

for every $n = 1, 2, \cdots$.

Then

$$\sum_{n=1}^{\infty} (|a_n| + |b_n|) \leq \frac{1}{2}\sum_{n=1}^{\infty} (\alpha_n^2 + \beta_n^2) + \sum_{n=1}^{\infty} \frac{1}{n^2} < \infty. \quad \blacksquare$$

It follows that the Fourier series of g converges absolutely uniformly and by Corollary 1 to Theorem 5, to be proved later, it converges to g at every point where g is differentiable. It follows that it converges uniformly to g.

Moreover, for every $\epsilon > 0$, there is an n such that

$$\int_a^b \left[g(x) - \left(\frac{1}{2}a_0 + \sum_{k=1}^{n} (a_k \cos kx + b_k \sin kx)\right)\right]^2 dx < \frac{\epsilon^2}{4}.$$

We need the simple fact that if f is Riemann integrable on $[a, b]$ and $\eta > 0$ there is a quasilinear g such that

$$\int_a^b (f-g)^2 < \eta.$$

Now, let f be periodic and Riemann integrable on $[-\pi, \pi]$. Let $\epsilon > 0$. There is a quasilinear periodic g such that

$$\int_a^b (f-g)^2 < \frac{\epsilon}{4}.$$

By the remark after Lemma 2, there is a trigonometric polynomial

$$t(x) = c_0 + \sum_{k=1}^{\infty} (c_k \cos kx + d_k \sin kx)$$

such that

$$\int_a^b (g-t)^2 < \frac{\epsilon}{4}.$$

By the triangle inequality,

$$\int_a^b (f-t)^2 < \epsilon.$$

This proves the

Theorem 3

The trigonometric functions form a closed orthonormal system on $[-\pi, \pi]$.

It follows that if two continuous functions have the same Fourier series they are identical. In particular, we have

$$|x| = \frac{\pi}{2} - \frac{4}{\pi}\left(\cos x + \frac{\cos 3x}{9} + \frac{\cos 5x}{25} + \cdots\right).$$

4. THE RIEMANN LOCALIZATION THEOREM

Let f be Riemann integrable on $[-\pi, \pi]$, and let

$$\frac{a_0}{2} + \sum_{n=1}^{\infty} (a_n \cos nx + b_n \sin nx)$$

be its Fourier series.

We let

$$s_n(x) = \frac{a_0}{2} + \sum_{k=1}^{n} (a_k \cos kx + b_k \sin kx),$$

for every $n = 0, 1, 2, \cdots$.

By the definition of the Fourier coefficients, we obtain

$$\begin{aligned} s_n(x) &= \frac{1}{2\pi} \int_{-\pi}^{\pi} f(t)\, dt + \sum_{k=1}^{n} \frac{1}{\pi} \int_{-\pi}^{\pi} f(t) \{\cos kx \cos kt + \sin kx \sin kt\}\, dt \\ &= \frac{1}{\pi} \int_{-\pi}^{\pi} f(t) \left\{\frac{1}{2} + \sum_{k=1}^{n} \cos k(x - t)\right\} dt. \end{aligned}$$

We need the fact that

$$\frac{1}{2} + \cos t + \cos 2t + \cdots + \cos nt = \frac{\sin (n + \frac{1}{2})t}{2 \sin \frac{1}{2}t}.$$

This formula may be proved by multiplying the series on the left by $2 \sin t/2$ and repeatedly using the identity

$$2 \cos A \sin B = \sin (A + B) - \sin (A - B).$$

Then,

$$\begin{aligned} &\sin \tfrac{1}{2}t + 2 \sin \tfrac{1}{2}t \cos t + \cdots + 2 \sin \tfrac{1}{2}t \cos nt \\ &= \sin \tfrac{1}{2}t + \sin (\tfrac{3}{2}t - \sin \tfrac{1}{2}t) + \cdots + [\sin (n + \tfrac{1}{2})t - \sin (n - \tfrac{1}{2})t] \\ &= \sin (n + \tfrac{1}{2})t, \end{aligned}$$

and the formula follows.

Thus,

$$s_n(x) = \frac{1}{\pi} \int_{-\pi}^{\pi} f(t) \frac{\sin (n + \frac{1}{2})(x - t)}{2 \sin \frac{1}{2}(x - t)}\, dt.$$

By a change of variable and the knowledge that f and the trigonometric functions have period 2π, we obtain

$$s_n(x) = \frac{1}{\pi} \int_{-\pi}^{\pi} f(x + t) \frac{\sin (n + \frac{1}{2})t}{2 \sin \frac{1}{2}t}\, dt.$$

A study of the convergence of the Fourier series of f is transferred to a study of the convergence of the sequence $\{s_n(x)\}$.

For every $x \in [-\pi, \pi]$, we show that for every $\delta > 0$, the convergence of $\{s_n(x)\}$ depends only on the values of f on the interval $(x - \delta, x + \delta)$.

What we shall prove is that

$$\lim_n \int_{-\pi}^{-\delta} f(x+t)\frac{\sin (n+\frac{1}{2})t}{2\sin \frac{1}{2}t}\,dt = 0$$

and

$$\lim_n \int_{\delta}^{\pi} f(x+t)\frac{\sin (n+\frac{1}{2})t}{2\sin \frac{1}{2}t}\,dt = 0.$$

On the interval $[\delta, \pi]$, $2\sin\frac{1}{2}t \geq 2\sin\frac{1}{2}\delta$, so that the function

$$g(t) = \frac{f(x+t)}{2\sin\frac{1}{2}t}$$

is Riemann integrable on this interval.

Our result will follow from

Lemma 3

If F is Riemann integrable on $[a, b] \subset [-\pi, \pi]$, and $\{k_n\}$ is an unbounded increasing sequence of positive numbers, then

$$\lim_n \int_a^b F(x)\cos k_n x\,dx = 0 \quad \textit{and} \quad \lim_n \int_a^b F(x)\sin k_n x\,dx = 0.$$

Proof

We first suppose that F is quasilinear. Then

$$\int_a^b F(x)\cos k_n x\,dx = \frac{1}{k_n}[F(b)\sin k_n b - F(a)\sin k_n a] - \frac{1}{k_n}\int_a^b F'(x)\cos k_n x\,dx.$$

Since the functions F and F' are bounded, and $\{1/k_n\}$ is a null sequence, the result follows.

Suppose F is Riemann integrable and let $\epsilon > 0$. Let g be quasilinear and such that

$$\int_a^b |F(x) - g(x)|\,dx < \epsilon.$$

Then

$$\left|\int_a^b F(x)\cos k_n x\,dx\right| \leq \int_a^b |F(x) - g(x)|\,dx + \left|\int_a^b g(x)\cos k_n x\,dx\right|.$$

It follows that

$$\limsup_n \left| \int_a^b F(x) \cos k_n x \, dx \right| \leq \epsilon.$$

Since this holds for every $\epsilon > 0$, the lemma has been proved. ∎
Applying this to our case,

$$\lim_n \int_\delta^\pi f(x + t) \frac{\sin (n + \frac{1}{2})t}{2 \sin \frac{1}{2}t} \, dt = 0.$$

Similarly,

$$\lim_n \int_{-\pi}^{-\delta} f(x + t) \frac{\sin (n + \frac{1}{2})t}{2 \sin \frac{1}{2}t} \, dt = 0.$$

We may state the

Theorem 4

If f is Riemann integrable and is identically zero on an open interval containing x, no matter how small the interval, the Fourier series of f converges to 0 at x.

Proof

Suppose $\delta > 0$ is such that f is identically zero on $(x - \delta, x + \delta)$. Then

$$\begin{aligned} s_n(x) &= \frac{1}{\pi} \int_{-\pi}^{\pi} f(x + t) \frac{\sin (n + \frac{1}{2}t)}{2 \sin \frac{1}{2}t} \, dt \\ &= \frac{1}{\pi} \int_{-\pi}^{-\delta} f(x + t) \frac{\sin (n + \frac{1}{2})t}{2 \sin \frac{1}{2}t} \, dt + \frac{1}{\pi} \int_\delta^\pi f(x + t) \frac{\sin (n + \frac{1}{2})t}{2 \sin \frac{1}{2}t} \, dt, \end{aligned}$$

It clearly follows that

$$\lim_n s_n(x) = 0. \quad ∎$$

Corollary 1

If f and g are Riemann integrable and equal in an open interval containing x, their Fourier series either both converge to the same value at x or both diverge at x.

5. CONVERGENCE OF FOURIER SERIES

There are many conditions under which the Fourier series of a function is known to converge. We shall present only one such condition.

Before doing this, it is convenient to replace the sequence $\{s_n(x)\}$ by a slightly modified sequence which we designate as $\{s_n^*(x)\}$.

We first note that

$$\frac{\sin(n+\frac{1}{2})t}{2\sin\frac{1}{2}t} = \frac{\sin nt}{2\tan\frac{1}{2}t} + \frac{1}{2}\cos nt$$
$$= \frac{\sin nt}{t} + \sin nt\left[\frac{1}{2\tan\frac{1}{2}t} - \frac{1}{t}\right] + \frac{1}{2}\cos nt.$$

Then

$$s_n(x) = \frac{1}{\pi}\int_{-\pi}^{\pi} f(x+t)\frac{\sin nt}{t}\,dt$$
$$+ \frac{1}{\pi}\int_{-\pi}^{\pi} f(x+t)\sin nt\left[\frac{1}{2\tan\frac{1}{2}t} - \frac{1}{t}\right]dt$$
$$+ \frac{1}{\pi}\int_{-\pi}^{\pi} \frac{1}{2} f(x+t)\cos nt\,dt.$$

The reader may show by using power series that $1/(2\tan 1/2t) - 1/t$ is a bounded function. It then follows that the last 2 integrals above converge to zero as n increases.

It follows that the Fourier series of f converges to s at x if and only if $\lim_n s_n^*(x) = s$, where

$$s_n^*(x) = \frac{1}{\pi}\int_{-\pi}^{\pi} f(x+t)\frac{\sin nt}{t}\,dt\,.$$

But,

$$\int_{-\pi}^{0} f(x+t)\frac{\sin nt}{t}\,dt = \int_{0}^{\pi} f(x-t)\frac{\sin nt}{t}\,dt,$$

so that

$$s_n^*(x) = \frac{1}{\pi}\int_{-0}^{\pi}\{f(x+t)+f(x-t)\}\frac{\sin nt}{t}\,dt.$$

Moreover,

$$\lim_n \frac{2}{\pi}\int_0^{\pi}\frac{\sin nt}{t}\,dt = 1.$$

We have thus shown that

$$\lim_n s_n^*(x) = s$$

if and only if

$$\lim_n \int_0^{\pi}[f(x+t)+f(x-t)-2s]\frac{\sin nt}{t}\,dt = 0.$$

Suppose, now, that f is continuous at x, and for some $\delta > 0$,

$$\int_0^\delta |f(x+t) + f(x-t) - 2f(x)| \frac{dt}{t} = \lim_{\zeta \to 0} \int_\zeta^\delta |f(x+t) + f(x-t) - 2f(x)| \frac{dt}{t} < \infty.$$

Let $\epsilon > 0$. There is an $\eta > 0$ such that

$$\int_0^\eta |f(x) + t) + f(x-t) - 2f(x)| \frac{dt}{t} < \epsilon.$$

Then, for all $n = 1, 2, \cdots$

$$\int_0^\eta |f(x+t) + f(x-t) - 2f(x)| \frac{\sin nt}{t} dt < \epsilon.$$

But

$$\lim_n \int_\eta^\delta \frac{|f(x+t) + f(x-t) - 2f(x)|}{t} \sin nt \, dt = 0.$$

It follows that

$$\lim_n \int_0^\delta |f(x+t) + f(x-t) - 2f(x)| \frac{\sin nt}{t} dt = 0.$$

and the Fourier series of f converges to $f(x)$ at x.

We have proved

Theorem 5

If f is Riemann integrable on $[-\pi, \pi]$, continuous at x, and there is a $\delta > 0$ such that

$$\int_0^\delta |f(x+t) + f(x-t) - 2f(x)| \frac{dt}{t} < \infty,$$

then the Fourier series of f converges to $f(x)$ at x.

Suppose f is differentiable at x. Then there is an M and a $\delta > 0$ such that $0 < t < \delta$ implies

$$\frac{|f(x+t) - f(x)|}{t} < M \quad \text{and} \quad \frac{|f(x-t) - f(x)|}{t} < M.$$

The condition of Theorem 5 is then satisfied by f at x. We thus have

Corollary 1

If f is Riemann integrable on $[-\pi, \pi]$ and differentiable at x, then the Fourier series of f converges to $f(x)$ at x.

6. (C, 1) SUMMABILITY OF FOURIER SERIES

If f is differentiable at x, we have shown that the Fourier series of f converges at x to $f(x)$. This is not always true for continuous functions. There are examples of continuous functions whose Fourier series do not converge everywhere. However, these examples are fairly complicated, and we shall not give them. We point out that it was not known until this year whether or not the Fourier series of every continuous function must converge at some points.

Although the sequence, $\{s_n(x)\}$, of partial sums of the Fourier series of a continuous function need not converge everywhere, it is a remarkable fact that for every periodic continuous f, of period 2π, the associated sequence $\{\sigma_n(x)\}$, of averages of $\{s_n(x)\}$ converges uniformly to f.

For every $n = 0, 1, 2, \cdots$,

$$\sigma_n(x) = \frac{1}{n+1}\{s_0(x) + s_1(x) + \cdots + s_n(x)\}.$$

Now,

$$s_n(x) = \frac{1}{\pi}\int_{-\pi}^{\pi} f(x+t)\,\frac{\sin(n+\frac{1}{2})t}{2\sin\frac{1}{2}t}\,dt.$$

To obtain $\sigma_n(x)$, we compute the sum $\sin(1/2)t + \sin(3/2)t + \cdots + \sin(n+1/2)t$.

Multiplying by $2\sin 1/2(t)$ and repeatedly using

$$2\sin A\sin B = \cos(A-B) - \cos(A+B),$$

we obtain

$$2\sin\tfrac{1}{2}t[\sin\tfrac{1}{2}t + \sin\tfrac{3}{2}t + \cdots + \sin(n+\tfrac{1}{2})t] = 1 - \cos(n+1)t.$$

Then,

$$\sin\frac{1}{2}t + \sin\frac{3}{2}t + \cdots + \sin\left(n+\frac{1}{2}\right)t = \frac{1-\cos(n+1)t}{2\sin\frac{1}{2}t}$$

$$= \frac{\sin^2\frac{1}{2}(n+1)t}{\sin\frac{1}{2}t}.$$

This yields the expression

$$\sigma_n(x) = \frac{1}{2\pi(n+1)}\int_{-\pi}^{\pi} f(x+t)\left[\frac{\sin\frac{1}{2}(n+1)t}{\sin\frac{1}{2}t}\right]^2 dt.$$

We first note that

$$\frac{1}{2\pi(n+1)}\int_{-\pi}^{\pi}\left[\frac{\sin\frac{1}{2}(n+1)t}{\sin\frac{1}{2}t}\right]^2 dt = 1,$$

since the left hand side is the average of terms each of which equals 1.

The reason why the $\{\sigma_n(x)\}$ behave better than the $\{s_n(x)\}$ is that the functions $\{[\sin\frac{1}{2}(n+1)t]/(\sin\frac{1}{2}t)\}^2$ are nonnegative, while the functions $[\sin(n+\frac{1}{2})t]/[\sin\frac{1}{2}t]$ are oscillatory.

Let $\delta > 0$. Then, for $\pi \geq |t| \geq \delta$,

$$\frac{1}{2\pi(n+1)}\left[\frac{\sin\frac{1}{2}(n+1)t}{\sin\frac{1}{2}t}\right]^2 \leq \frac{1}{2\pi(n+1)\sin^2\frac{1}{2}\delta}.$$

Suppose, now, that f is continuous and periodic of period 2π. Then

$$|f(x)-\sigma_n(x)| = \left|f(x) - \frac{1}{2\pi(n+1)}\int_{-\pi}^{\pi} f(x+t)\left[\frac{\sin\frac{1}{2}(n+1)t}{\sin\frac{1}{2}t}\right]^2 dt\right|$$

$$\leq \frac{1}{2\pi(n+1)}\int_{-\pi}^{\pi}|f(x)-f(x+t)|\left[\frac{\sin\frac{1}{2}(n+1)t}{\sin\frac{1}{2}t}\right]^2 dt.$$

There is an M such that $|f(u)| \leq M$, for every real u. Let $\epsilon > 0$. There is a $\delta > 0$ such that for all real u, v, with $|u-v| < \delta$, we have $|f(u)-f(v)| < \epsilon/(4\pi)$.

Let N be such that $n > N$ implies

$$\frac{1}{2\pi(n+1)\sin^2\frac{1}{2}\delta} < \frac{\epsilon}{8\pi M}.$$

For $n > N$, and x real,

$$|f(x)-\sigma_n(x)| \leq \frac{1}{2\pi(n+1)}\int_{-\delta}^{\delta}|f(x)-f(x+t)|\left[\frac{\sin\frac{1}{2}(n+1)t}{\sin\frac{1}{2}(t)}\right]^2 dt$$

$$+\frac{1}{2\pi(n+1)}\int_{\delta\leqslant|t|<\pi}|f(x)-f(x+t)|\left[\frac{\sin\frac{1}{2}(n+1)t}{\sin\frac{1}{2}nt}\right]^2 dt$$

$$\leq \frac{\epsilon}{4\pi}\cdot 2\delta + 2M\cdot\frac{\epsilon}{8\pi M} = \epsilon.$$

We have accordingly proved Fejer's theorem.

Theorem 6

If f is continuous and periodic of period 2π, the sequence $\{\sigma_n(x)\}$ of averages of the partial sums of the Fourier series of f converges uniformly to f on the real line.

The astute reader will note that the proof of Fejer's theorem and of the uniform convergence of Bernstein polynomials follows the same general ideas.

EXERCISES

1.1 Find 4 polynomials that are orthonormal on $[a, b]$.

1.2 Find an infinite number of functions that are orthonormal on $(0, \infty)$.

1.3 Is there an interval on which x, x^2, x^3 are orthonormal?

1.4 A system of continuous functions is said to be linearly independent if every finite linear combination, with nonzero coefficients is not identically zero. Show that every orthonormal system is linearly independent.

2.1 Which functions of period 2π have Fourier series involving only sine terms.

2.2 Obtain the Fourier series of the function which is e^x on $-\pi \leq x < \pi$.

2.3 Obtain the Fourier series of $|\sin x|$.

3.1 Given an orthornormal system on $[a, b]$ which is not complete, show that functions can be added to the system so that the enlarged system is a complete orthonormal system.

3.2 Using the fact that every continuous periodic function, of period 2π, is the uniform limit of a sequence of functions of the form

$$c_0 + \sum_{n=1}^{\infty} (c_n \cos nx + d_n \sin nx),$$

prove the Weierstrass polynomial approximation theorem.

4.1 If f is of bounded variation on $[-\pi, \pi]$, and $\{a_n\}$, $\{b_n\}$ are its Fourier coefficients, show that

$$a_n = O(1/n) \quad \text{and} \quad b_n = O(1/n).$$

4.2 A series $\sum_{n=0}^{\infty} a_n$ is said to be Riemann summable to s if

$$\lim_{h\to 0}\left[a_0 + \sum_{n=1}^{\infty} a_n \left(\frac{\sin nh}{nh}\right)^2\right] = s.$$

Show that if $\sum_{n=1}^{\infty} a_n$ converges, with sum s, then it is Riemann summable to s.

4.3 With a Fourier series

$$\frac{a_0}{2} + \sum_{n=1}^{\infty} (a_n \cos nx + b_n \sin nx),$$

associate the twice integrated series

$$\frac{a_0}{2} x^2 + bx + c - \frac{1}{n^2}\sum_{n=1}^{\infty} (a_n \cos nx + b_n \sin nx).$$

This series converges uniformly to a function F. Using the result of Exercise 4.2, show that if the Fourier series of f converges to f at x_0 then the generalized second derivative of F exists and is equal to $f(x_0)$.

5.1 Discuss the convergence and uniform convergence of the series

$$\sum_{n=1}^{\infty} \frac{1}{n} \sin nx.$$

5.2 The functions

$$D_n(t) = \frac{1}{\pi}\frac{\sin (n + \frac{1}{2})t}{2 \sin \frac{1}{2}(t)}, \quad n = 1, 2, \cdots$$

are called the Dirichlet kernels. Plot the curves of the first 4 Dirichlet kernels.

5.3 Show that the sequence

$$\int_{-\pi}^{\pi} D_n(t)\, dt$$

diverges to infinity.

5.4 Show that if the coefficients of a Fourier series form a decreasing sequence, then the series converges except possibly at multiples of π.

6.1 Find $\sigma_n(x)$ for the series $\sum_{n=1}^{\infty} \sin nx$ and discuss the convergence of the sequence $\sigma_n(x)$.

6.2 Do the same as in Exercise 6.1 for

$$\sin x + \sin 3x + \cdots + \sin (2n - 1)x + \cdots$$

6.3 Show that for every continuous f, of period 2π, the Fourier series of f is Abel summable to f.

6.4 Show that for every continuous f, of period 2π, the Fourier series of f is Riemann summable to f.

INDEX